THE BUILDING SOCIETY VALUER

THE BUILDING SOCIETY VALUER

Including the survey and valuation of houses and flats for owner-occupation

by

RICHARD J. BYROM

J.P., B.A.(Arch.), A.R.I.B.A., F.S.V.A., F.C.I.Arb.

1979

THE ESTATES GAZETTE LIMITED
151, Wardour Street · London · W1V 4BN

First Published 1979

© RICHARD J. BYROM, 1979

Text set in 10/11 pt VIP Melior, printed and bound
in Great Britain at the Pitman Press, Bath

Acknowledgments

I am grateful to H. Brompton, F.R.I.C.S., Chairman of the Building Societies Association Panel of Surveyors, and to my partner M. A. Taylor, B.Sc.(Est.Man.), A.R.I.C.S., both of whom were kind enough to read the book in manuscript form and make many helpful observations. Also to Mrs. Janet Grundy, who did most of the typing, and to the various publishers who have allowed me to include quotations from their publications, as refered to in the text and bibliography.

Introduction

At the present time some 800,000 building society valuations are undertaken each year and there must be few firms of chartered surveyors or incorporated valuers whose work does not include at least the occasional building society valuation survey for mortgage purposes, and some practices have several valuers working full-time on these and nothing else. Similar work also comes from insurance companies, finance houses, large concerns offering mortgage facilities to their staffs, local authorities and individuals granting private mortgages.

Because the vast majority of building society valuation surveys are of residential properties for owner-occupation, only this type of property is discussed in detail, although some brief notes on valuations of other types of property for mortgage purposes are included.

Many recently qualified surveyors and valuers are likely to find themselves entrusted with building society surveys at an early stage in their professional careers. This book should help them to approach the work with confidence. At the other end of the scale, it should be of interest to the experienced practitioner, who will no doubt compare his own approach to the work with that described here.

I hope too that the book will give some insight to the many members of staff of building society offices who send instructions to valuers but to whom what happens after those instructions have been sent, and before the valuer's report arrives back, remains something of a mystery.

Perhaps members of the public who pay a fee to a building society for a valuation report will learn something of the wide background knowledge a building society valuer must have to do his job effectively, and precisely what job it is that he does.

The terms surveyor and valuer in this book are both used to describe the same person; the property is surveyed in order that it may be valued. I have used the term valuer in the title and generally in the text because most building societies (and the Building Societies' Association) prefer this usage, largely because of the problems of differentiating between the building society valuation and a structural survey.

Byrom Hill,
Manchester and Bury.

9th May, 1979.

valuation PS 99-115

Contents

Chapter 1

Society and Valuer

1.1. The Building Society Movement

The Building Society movement commenced in the mid-19th century. A hundred and twenty-five years or so later there are about 340 building societies, with total assets in the region of £40,000,000,000, making about 750,000 advances to borrowers by way of mortgage per year.

Present trends are for the larger societies to get larger and for smaller societies to amalgamate with larger ones, so that some 300 of the societies hold only a little over 5% of the total assets and the 140 smaller societies account for only 0.3% of all advances.

Building societies are controlled by the Building Societies Act 1962, of which section 1(1) defines the purpose of a building society in the following terms:

> "1(1) The purpose for which the society may be established under this Act is that of raising, by the subscriptions of the members, a stock or fund for making advances to members out of the funds of the society upon security by way of mortgage of freehold or leasehold estate."

By section 4(i) of the Act every building society is to have rules which shall set out, *inter alia*, "the purposes to which the funds of the society are to be applied."

At first sight this might appear a curious requirement, having regard to the sole statutory purpose set out in section 1(1), but the point is that a society may wish to confine itself more narrowly, for example to residential property only, or to borrowing-members of a limited kind.

In practice building societies currently tend to limit advances to residential property for owner-occupation, or at least to property which has some residential accommodation within it.

In any event section 21 of the Act severely limits the amounts of advances that may be made to bodies corporate or advances in excess of £5,000 (subsequently raised to £20,000).

A society is not permitted to advance money on the primary

1

security of a second mortgage, unless the prior mortgage is in favour of the society making the advance. Contributory mortgages are not permitted except that section 8(5) of the Housing Act 1964 permits contributory mortgages when the borrower is a housing society and all the contributing lenders are building societies.

The building societies are committed to the concept of home-ownership, and the proportion of the nation's houses in owner-occupation continues to rise. There are few things that raise a person's self-respect more than owning his own home. A home-owning democracy is almost certainly the most stable form of society. About 95% of the finance for home-purchase is provided by the building societies and thus they bear, and accept, a large degree of social responsibility. There is normally not enough money available to satisfy the demand for advances, yet, notwithstanding this, most societies as a matter of policy do not limit their lending policies to modern property but are usually prepared to lend on older properties providing their surveyor is able to advise that the houses provide adequate security for the advance required, often granting advances of 80% or more of the valuation, as opposed to the usual commerical limit of two-thirds of the valuation.

Priority is often given to first-time purchasers, although this can rebound by making it difficult for second-time purchasers to "up-market", thus reducing the number of suitable houses available to first-time purchasers.

Since 1975 the building societies have operated a local authority support scheme whereby loans are made to people who would otherwise obtain loans from local authorities, a scheme which in some areas has been misused as a means of queue-jumping. So far as the valuer is concerned, his approach and valuation must be exactly the same for local authority support scheme cases as for others.

1.2. Types of Mortgage

The valuer's report and valuation will be the same, whatever type of mortgage is envisaged. However, the valuer should be aware of the different types of mortgage. These fall into two groups as follows:-

A. *Mortgages Usually Granted by Building Societies.*
Annuity or repayment mortgage. This is the most common type of mortgage, where a fixed periodic payment is made, consist-

ing partly of repayment of the amount borrowed and partly of interest on the amount which has not yet been repaid. The debt reduces year by year until it is finally repaid. The periodic payment varies from time to time with any change in the rate of interest charged.

Endowment mortgage. With an endowment mortgage, none of the loan is repaid until the proceeds of an endowment assurance policy are paid over in a single sum, either at the end of the policy period or on the death of the life-assured, if earlier. Interest is charged throughout the mortgage period on the whole of the amount borrowed.

Option mortgage. The option mortgage scheme is designed to help people with modest incomes to buy their own homes by giving them benefits roughly equal to those that are available to people with higher incomes who can claim relief from income tax on that part of their income that they use to pay mortgage interest. The right to tax relief on mortgage interest is given up, but, instead, part of the interest on the loan is paid by Government subsidy. The scheme is operated by most building societies, life assurance offices, friendly societies, local authorities and other institutions who make home loans. Two prior conditions must be fulfilled: (a) that the home is used or will be used within twelve months from the date of the mortgage wholly or partly as the borrower's only or main residence or the only or main residence of qualifying relatives; (b) that the amount of the loan, together with the amount outstanding on certain existing property loans which are eligible for option mortgage subsidy or for tax relief, does not exceed £25,000. Option mortgages are available for buying or building a home, buying the land on which to build a home, converting a building into a home, altering, enlarging, repairing or improving a home, purchasing the freehold of a leasehold property, or to replace an earlier loan for any of these purposes.

B. *Mortgages More Usual in the Commercial Sphere.*

Fixed-instalment mortgage. With a fixed-instalment mortgage, a fixed capital sum is repaid each year, plus interest on the balance remaining unpaid.

Standing mortgage. Sometimes lenders are willing to make a loan with no provision in the mortgage agreement for regular repayment of any part of the amount borrowed. This arrangement is known as a standing mortgage, and interest is charged on the whole of the amount borrowed throughout the mortgage period, as in an endowment mortgage.

Deferred-payment mortgage. A deferred-payment mortgage is one where part of the payment due in the early years can be deferred until later in the life of the mortgage, when the probability is that the borrower's earnings will have increased and he will be in a better position to afford higher payments.

Mixed mortgage. Sometimes a mortgage is granted consisting partly of an endowment or standing mortgage, partly of an annuity or repayment mortgage.

1.3. House Prices and the Economy

The relationship between house prices and earnings has been fairly stable in the post-war years, when house prices have averaged about three times average annual earnings, apart from a brief period in 1971–73 when house prices rose to the level of four times average annual earnings and subsequently fell back.

The rate of house price increases does not follow that of retail prices. In 1975 house prices increased at half the rate of that of retail prices. By 1978 this relationship had reversed with house prices rising at an annual rate of approximately 20% compared with a published rate of retail price inflation of about $7\frac{1}{2}$%.

Building societies are the largest institutional recipient of personal savings in the U.K., and this inevitably leads to considerable Government interest in the movement. For example, in June 1978 the building societies agreed, at the Government's request, to reduce their lending by 10% of the total in an endeavour to steady house prices. This attempt did not prove successful and it would appear that the limitation of funds does not affect house prices.

Societies need to take in about one third of the total personal savings market. They are in competition with other institutions and have to adjust the interest rates paid to savers from time to time to achieve their required share of the market. Any change in interest paid to savers is normally reflected in interest rates payable by borrowers, but this has not generally had any marked effect on house prices.

A major incentive to borrowers is that tax relief is currently available on mortgage payments up to a maximum eligible mortgage amount of £25,000. In July 1978 the General Secretary of the Labour Party made the following statement:

"The Labour Party has two established policies for mortgage

tax relief—to make relief available only against the standard rate of income tax, not the higher rates, and to reduce the maximum mortgage amount eligible for relief from its present £25,000 to a figure closer to average house prices (varied on a regional basis)."

If this were to come about it could affect prices at the upper end of the market. This approach contrasts with that of the Building Societies Association, who have requested the Chancellor of the Exchequer to increase the £25,000 ceiling to £40,000, which would probably have the converse effect.

The number of new households forming each year has been falling for some time, and this fall is likely to continue to about 160,000 a year during the 1980s. Many of these new households will be single-person households. There is a growing surplus of housing, and it is estimated that by the mid 1980s there may be as many as 1½ million houses not regularly occupied, although this will include a proportion of second homes. This is likely to reduce the demand for new building and may reduce the rate of increase of house prices.

1.4. Obtaining a Mortgage

The vast majority of houses in the U.K. are purchased with the assistance of a building society mortgage. To obtain a mortgage, a prospective purchaser makes application either direct to a building society branch office or to a building society agent. The society then checks that the required advance is within the lending limits and policy of the society at the time, taking into account:-

— the amount of advance required
— the term of years over which the mortgage is required
— the income of the applicant(s)
— the applicant's likely ability to keep up with repayments during the full term of the proposed mortgage.
— the status of the applicant
— the price, age, type and location of the property offered as security

If it appears that the required advance falls within the lending limits and policy of the society and the applicant is of suitable financial standing, instructions are sent to the society's valuer in the area where the property is situated. The valuer then visits the property and prepares his report, returning it to the society. If the report is satisfactory the society make a written offer of the advance to the applicant. A solicitor on the society's panel is instructed to act on behalf of the society: when the applicant's own solicitor is on the panel of the society granting the mortgage it is quite usual for him to act for both applicant and society. The solicitor checks that the title of the property to be mortgaged is in order, checks the surveyors description and plan against the description and plan in the deeds, and prepares the necessary mortgage deeds. A cheque is then issued by the society and completion takes place.

1.5. The Valuer—His Qualifications and Appointment

Section 25(1) of the Building Societies Act 1962 makes it the responsibility of the directors of the society to ensure that the adequacy of the security is properly assessed and that the security is properly and independently valued. The section reads as follows:

"25(1) It shall be the duty of every director of the building society to satisfy himself that the arrangements made for assessing the adequacy of the security to be taken in respect of advances to be made by the society are such as may be reasonably expected to ensure that:

(a) The adequacy of any security to be so taken will be assessed either by the directors of the society or by a director or other officer of the society who is competent to make the assessment, and

(b) There will be made available to every person who has to assess the adequacy of any security to be so taken an appropriate report as to the value of any freehold or leasehold estate comprised in the security and as to any matter likely to affect the value thereof."

Section 25(2) defines who may prepare the report, in the following terms:

"25(2) In paragraph (b) of the preceding sub-section the reference to an appropriate report, in relation to any freehold or leasehold estate, is a reference to a written report prepared and signed by a competent and prudent person who:

(a) is experienced in the matters relevant to the determination of the value of the estate, and

(b) is for the purposes of that paragraph not disqualified

by virtue of the following provisions of this section for reporting on that estate."

Sections 25(3) to 25(6) set out persons who may not prepare the valuation report. These are as follows:

A director of the society
The manager of the society
The secretary of the society
A person paid by the society for introducing the particular proposed borrower
A person with a financial interest in a contemporaneous sale or disposition of the property in question
A person getting a commission or gift for introducing the parties to the transaction.

✗The "appropriate report" must therefore be a written report, prepared and signed by a competent and prudent person, experienced in matters relevant to the determination of the value of the estate and who is not disqualified. The report must refer to the value of any freehold or leasehold estate comprised in the security and to any matter likely to affect is value.

In order that the directors of the Society may have some assurance that the appointed valuer is competent, they usually restrict appointments to persons who are fellows or associates of the Royal Institution of Chartered Surveyors or the Incorporated Society of Valuers and Auctioneers. In practice their valuation panels normally include firms, one or more of whose principals are so qualified. There are, however, examples of firms of appointed valuers with different professional qualifications; thus some societies have several firms of architect-valuers. Nor need the valuer have any professional qualifications, as sometimes happens in the case of a firm which has acted for a society for many years and may reasonably be considered to be qualified by experience. Many of the larger societies employ a number of staff surveyors who are on the permanent payroll of the society and who will normally be chartered surveyors or incorporated valuers. Besides being a competent and prudent person, the valuer must be experienced in matters relevant to the determination of the value of the estate: these matters are not defined, but it is suggested that they should cover experience in the locality involved and, where valuations of a specialist nature are concerned, such as agricultural property or licensed premises, there should be the appropriate specialist experience. Whilst a firm of valuers who are also active in the fields of estate agency are likely to be close to the pulse of the market, in areas where there is intense competition between agents there can be a deal of bitterness when one agent acting for a building society devalues a property another agent is selling. For this reason there is often merit in appointing a firm which deals entirely with professional work, rather than agency, to act for the building society, if such a firm exists in an area. The practice of appointing a firm of valuers from outside the area in which the property is situated is wasteful in travelling time and expenses, and local knowledge must be limited.

The report will normally be signed by a principal in the appointed firm of valuers, and specimen signatures of approved signatories will often be held by the building society. Some societies also require the report to be signed by the actual surveyor who carried out the survey.

The report must be a report on the value of the property and on any matter likely to affect the value thereof: what these last words cover is not at all clear and Wurtzburg and Mills (Building Society Law—Stevens & Sons) comment, "They can hardly mean that every report should mention supply and demand, inflation, slump, general elections, nuclear war and so on; probably they are intended to mean any known things, which, though not reflected in the present value, are likely to bear upon it later, regard being given also to the likelihood or otherwise that the things themselves will actually happen."

It is accepted within the building society movement and the surveying profession that what is required is a "valuation survey" which does not involve the detailed structural investigations which are appropriate to a "structural survey". This is reflected in the nature of the standard report forms printed by societies and in the level of the scale of fees for building society inspections.

The disqualifications to being a valuer for a society cover directors of the society (who traditionally often used to carry out valuations), an agent of the society who introduces the mortgage business, the vendor of the property (or possibly the builder or developer or a relative of the vendor who has a financial interest in the sale), or the vendor's estate agent.

Most societies appoint one or more firms of valuers for a particular geographical area and send their valuation instructions to these firms. In other cases, except where there is a staff surveyor, the local manager of the society sends the valuation instructions to such local firm as he sees fit. In the present writer's opinion there is considerable advantage in the appointment of firms of valuers being made by the Head Office of the Society.

Any valuer who prepares a report for a building society whilst disqualified from doing so lays himself open to a fine or imprisonment by virtue of section 25(7) of the Act. In carrying out his duties, a surveyor is bound to use reasonable care and skill and he will be answerable in damages for any failure in this respect. Thus, where a society suffers loss on a mortgage owing to the negligence of their surveyor in making a valuation of the mortgaged property, the society can recover its loss as damages against the surveyor, notwithstanding any provision in the rules or in any contract indemnifying him. (S. 92)

1.6. Planning the Day

An average valuer can do about five valuation surveys in a day, less if they include very large properties or where distances are great, more where the properties are small and near to his office or where only re-inspections are required.

Most instructions to value will arrive in the morning's post. Some will come in the second post and others perhaps by hand from a local building society office. Other instructions will come over the telephone, often with a request that they be treated as urgent.

If the valuer is going to work efficiently, he must plan his day in advance, with the objectives of ensuring that he will be able to get into all the properties he visits, thus avoiding abortive journeys, and keeping travelling to a minimum. This is important: not only is petrol expensive, but the valuer cannot afford to waste time. The aim is to get the reports back to the society in the minimum time which is compatible with reasonable office efficiency. An office should aim at a norm of five days. Some reports will be done in less time than this, some will take longer, either because of access problems or because further information on some point is awaited; or perhaps because a second opinion from another member of the office is being sought.

Each morning the instructions that have come in that morning, and those which came in during the latter part of the previous day, will be allocated between the surveyors in the office, office records having first been checked to see if the property has previously been surveyed. Some offices allocate surveys by area and this is generally the most efficient method, especially when covering a large region.

The valuer, having got his list, sets about making appointments, normally planning for a day or two ahead. Some instructions will have an agent's name and if one is lucky the agent will have the key. Instructions should, whenever possible, include the vendor's telephone number. This often yields no reply until after the working day is finished. In other cases no agent or telephone number is given, merely the vendor's name. A look in the telephone directory may reveal a number but, if not, an appointment letter is essential if an abortive journey is to be avoided. Sent by first-class post the letter will probably arrive after the vendors have gone to work, so the appointment must be for two days hence. A standard letter or card is usual, with blanks that can be filled in.

A suitable standard letter might read:

"We are instructed to value the above property in connection with a mortgage application by ....
Our Mr. ....proposes to carry out the survey at about .... a.m./p.m. on ....
Please will you arrange for someone to be available at the property at that time or a key to be left at our office before 9.30 a.m. on that day. If this is not possible please telephone this office as soon as possible to make alternative arrangements."

Properties under construction can normally be inspected at any time, although often the information required is not available from the site agent and one is referred to a sales negotiator who attends at a caravan or show house for only a limited number of hours each day. In any event it is generally useless to visit new sites at lunch-time or after about 4.30 p.m.

A valuer will need to plan his calls so as to avoid alternate appointments at opposite extremities of the town. Beside making an appointment the valuer will also look out any previous information on the property and check the office records for values of similar nearby-houses. If the property has recently been surveyed by the office for another party the time necessary for the visit can be significantly reduced, especially if a plan has already been done.

1.7. The Valuer's Equipment

Mobility is essential. The surveyor is going to be out of his office for much of the day and a significant amount of time will be spent travelling. A reliable car is essential and money spent on regular servicing is money well spent, since a failure to start in the morning or a breakdown during the day can totally disrupt a carefully planned schedule. Because a fair proportion of a surveyor's time is spent in his car, comfort and a good heater are important. A spacious boot is also essential to carry survey equipment.

Arrangements for payment of staff motoring expenses differ from firm to firm but a common arrangement is for a mileage rate to be paid. Where this is done it is essential that the surveyor keeps daily records of his business mileage. In most cases the surveyor will attend at his office first thing in the morning to deal with his paper work and telephone calls and will be back at the office in the late afternoon to sign reports. Where this is the usual pattern the mileage log only needs to record the mileage at the commencement of the day, the areas visited and the mileage at the end of the day. Where mileage charges are being passed on to the building society in respect of particular properties, it is desirable that the mileage in these cases should be recorded at the time of survey.

Besides his car, the valuer needs to have the following equipment with him.

Street maps of the towns in which surveys are carried out.
1/50,000 Ordnance Survey maps of the area.
Mileage log.
Visiting cards.
Spare appointment cards.
Clip board.
Report forms.
Squared paper for plans.
Tracing paper.
Pencil.
India rubber.
Scale rule.
Probe.
Moisture meter.
Hand lamp.
Spirit level (about 1 metre long).
Plumb bob and line.
30 m (100 ft) tape.
Cleaning cloth.
Surveying pins.

2 m (6 ft) folding staff.
String line.
Ranging rod.
Instant camera and film (if instructed by societies who require photographs).
Pocket calculator.
Waterproofs.
Wellingtons.

If the surveyor also does structural surveys in the course of his business he will also carry folding ladders, equipment for raising manhole covers, drain dye, tools for cutting floor traps, binoculars, magnifying glass, specimen containers, safety helmet and overalls. These additional items of equipment may be of assistance to the building society surveyor on very infrequent occasions but are not essential to his work.

1.9. Doing the Survey

On arrival at an occupied property the valuer may well be asked to give some proof of his identity. A visiting card should suffice, although in some urban areas an identification card with photograph may be worthwhile.

Where a property is only occupied by a child the valuer may deem it prudent to make arrangements to call again when an adult is present.

Dogs occasionally present a hazard. Even the friendliest of family pets is not always too pleased to have a strange surveyor letting himself into the house unaccompanied. Caution is recommended.

Infectious diseases are another hazard. Not infrequently the valuer will be greeted with the welcoming advice that someone in the house has some infectious disease. If the valuer has an expectant wife or very young baby he may well wish to postpone the survey or get a colleague to do it.

When inspecting properties under construction, especially blocks of flats, normal site safety precautions should be observed and a helmet worn. When surveying unoccupied property, especially in isolated locations, the valuer should ensure that someone knows where he has gone. Work involving above average risk such as inspections of constricted sub-floor spaces in unoccupied property should not be attempted without an assistant in attendance.

If the weather is such that rain seems likely it is best to do the outside work first whilst it is still dry. If it is raining, start with the inside, in the hope that the rain may stop within the next half-hour! When the valuer has an assistant with him it is usually easier if the assistant deals with the plan, leaving the valuer to record details of the property itself.

The inspection must include all the rooms, the external elevations, all the outbuildings and grounds and a look at the type and condition of neighbouring properties, together with an assessment of the type of neighbourhood and available amenities. It is not usual to inspect roof or sub-floor spaces on a building society valuation, nor to lift manhole covers.

Traditionally, surveyors made their site notes in a field book but in the writer's opinion notes are best made on a form similar to (or even on a photocopy of) the form which will ultimately be sent to the society. This avoids taking site notes and having to re-write them for typing. Site notes straight on to a dictating machine are difficult, as the surveyor can rarely dictate a complete final report straight off and his dictated site notes will have to be transcribed before he can write out or dictate his final report for the society. The more information that can be put down in its final form whilst still at the property, the more accurate the report is likely to be.

The vendor who insists on following the valuer round and keeps up a constant verbal barrage is a regular nuisance. In any event the valuer should not enter into discussions with the vendor, in spite of the inevitable requests for information he will receive.

Chapter 2

The Report

2.1. The Report Form

Each society has its own report form. So have many insurance companies, although some merely give a list of points to be covered in the valuer's report.

Report forms come in all shapes and sizes, quarto, A4, foolscap, one-sided, two-sided or folded to give four sides. They come in different colours, with different coloured copies for different destinations. Some societies require merely one copy, but three is more general, one for the local office, one for the head office, and a copy giving descriptive information only for the solicitor's use. The valuer also requires an office copy and there is usually an additional form provided for this.

Some societies provide their valuers with a pad of forms, others send out forms for each individual survey, often with the instructions to the valuer printed on the front of the form. This latter system can lead to problems: even if the valuer manages not to drop the form in the mud or to spill his tea on it, there is still the risk that a typing error in the valuation figure will result in obvious scratching out of the one place on the report where it is important that there should be no indication that an alteration has been made.

The Building Society Institute, in its book "Mortgage Lending Procedure—A model" publishes a "Model Valuer's Report". This is a four-page document with "Valuation Instructions" on the first page followed by three pages of boxes (21 in all) to be completed by the valuer. A useful point made by the Research Group who prepared the form (none of whom was a surveyor!) is that they do not expect the valuer to check the information on tenure supplied by the applicant but invite him to report any apparent discrepancies of which he is aware. Similarly, the valuer is not required to make legal enquiries but is invited to report any apparent or suspected rights of way, easements, etc., affecting the property.

In general one finds that the smaller the society is the more information it requires, the more complex the questions on the form and the more questions against which the valuer must write "not applicable". Many of the questions are largely irrelevant to the grant of a mortgage and one suspects that large sections of many of these forms are never in fact read by anybody. Complicated forms are counter-productive and not in the interests of the society since valuers, being human, will generally tend to deal with the more simple reports first.

In the writer's opinion all the information which a building society needs in order to grant a mortgage can comfortably go on one side of one A4 sheet. This sheet should be thin enough to permit carbons to be used easily so that all the copies can be typed at one time. Some method must be devised to limit the information which goes to the solicitor to the descriptive matter only, either by having one of the copies rather shorter than the others and omitting the valuer's recommendations on the solicitor's copy or by some other means. Societies will no doubt be considering the type of form which produces duplicates without the need to use separate sheets of carbon paper. This allows blanks to occur on some of the copies where necessary but may prove difficult if there is insufficient space on the front of the form—using carbon paper it is easy to turn over and continue on the reverse side.

The information which the society needs on its report form is as follows:

The name of the society.
The address of the society, to which the report is to be sent.
The society's reference.
The name of the valuer.
The valuer's address.
The valuer's telephone number.
The valuer's reference.
Name(s) of borrower(s).
The postal address of the property being valued.
A brief description of the type of property.
The tenure and ground rent or chief rent.
The age of the property.
The construction of the property—walls, floors, roof.
The accommodation on each floor.
The outbuildings and grounds.
Services—water, electricity, gas, sewerage, heating, kitchen
    fittings, sanitary fittings.
Potential paving and sewer liabilities.
The recommended insurance cover.

All the above information is descriptive. The remaining

information is more subjective and has the nature of confidential observations to the society. It includes:

A note on the location and surroundings.

The structural and decorative condition.

The valuer's observations on any other matters he considers relevant to the mortgage, such as easements, town planning matters, etc.

In the case of new houses a note on the stage of construction reached, the name of the builder and whether or not N.H.B.C. registered.

The valuer's recommendation as to the suitability of the property for mortgage in terms of percentage advance and term of years or categorisation of the property, depending on the requirements of the particular society. A schedule of any undertakings, retentions or special conditions to be attached to the mortgage offer.

The valuation.

The date.

The fee, mileage charge, V.A.T. and a total.

The signature of a principal of the valuer's firm, with the name of the firm typed or rubber stamped beneath it and a statement that the valuer's firm are not disqualified from reporting on the property by virtue of the provisions of Section 25 of the Building Societies Act 1962.

The other information required by the society can best be shown on the plan and covers the location, orientation and dimensions of the site.

Many societies ask for other information which is sometimes largely irrelevent, but takes the valuer time and effort to provide.

A separate form is needed for further inspections. These may be either re-valuations, or re-inspections.

Re-valuations are Necessary in the Following Cases.

Where a borrower requires a re-advance or larger advance on a property.

Where a borrower wishes to take a further advance to assist with the costs of extensions, improvements, repairs, purchase of additional land, purchase of the freehold, etc.

In the event of matrimonial separation, where one party is to purchase the share of the other.

In the event of the property coming into the possession of the society, when a forced-sale valuation is needed.

Re-Inspections are Necessary in the Following Cases.

In connection with stage payments during initial construction of a property or during the construction of an extension.

To certify satisfactory completion of a new property or of an extension to an existing property.

To check that work which was the subject of a retention has been satisfactorily completed.

Some societies have a second form for re-valuations and re-inspections, whereas other societies require the further information in the form of a letter only. It is probably easier to have a form and one can be devised which will deal with any of the above occurrences, again on one side only of an A4 sheet. The following headings are appropriate:-

Name of society.
Address of society.
Society's reference.
Name of valuer.
Address of valuer.
Telephone number of valuer.
Valuer's reference.
Name(s) of borrower(s).
Address of property.
Description of property.
Tenure.
Age.
Valuer's report, on proposals and/or current position.
Potential paving and sewer charges.
Recommended insurance cover (on completion of work).
Valuer's recommendation.
The value of the property in present condition.
Value of property on completion of proposed work, etc.
Survey fee, mileage, V.A.T. and total.
Valuer's signature with name of firm typed or rubber-stamped beneath it.
Date.

2.2. Tenure

Property may be held either freehold, with or without chief rent, leasehold for a term of years with an annual rent, or on a short tenancy. Some properties will have a combination of all three. For example, a semi-detached house may be leasehold for the residue of 999 years with a nominal ground rent, but a portion of land extending the rear garden and acquired at a later date may be freehold, whilst the house may have a garage situated on a near-by piece of ground which is held on an annual tenancy subject to a ground rent. In this case the garage does not provide suitable security for a mortgage advance and must therefore be excluded from the valuation for mortgage purposes. Examples like this are not uncommon and the omission of a garage from the security may make quite a marked reduction in the valuation of the property. A similar but more acute problem arises where a septic tank is located on land held on an annual tenancy: where this is the case it is likely that the surveyor will have to recommend that the property is unsuitable for mortgage advance, unless the septic tank could be re-sited if necessary within the freehold or long leasehold curtilage of the property, in which case the mortgage would have to be subject to a retention amounting to the cost of re-siting the septic tank and subject to statutory approvals for the re-siting of the tank being obtained.

A common term of years for leases in the residential sector is 999 and in practical terms there is little difference between a freehold property with a nominal chief rent and a long leasehold property with nominal ground rent.

It is customary for valuation purposes to consider terms of 60 years or more as in perpetuity. However, where the lease on a property is less than 60 years at the time of valuation, this must be taken into account. The value of a property held on a short lease is likely to be diminishing and as the security for the mortgage must be adequate during the full term of the mortgage, any case where the remaining term of years will be less than 60 years at the end of the mortgage term requires special consideration as discussed in Chapter 5. There is no special virtue in the figure of 60 years; it merely represents the point beyond which, in normal cases, any differences are likely to be so small as not to be worth regarding.

Another popular term of years in the residential sector is 99. This is increasingly so in the case of current developments and on land which was previously in the ownership of a local authority, perhaps as a result of the Community Land Act. Thus there are, and will be, an increasing number of properties on the market with short terms needing special consideration. Assuming a 25 year mortgage term, any property on a 99 year lease which is more than 14 years old will come into this category.

The tenure of flats is discussed in Chapter 8. Town houses

forming part of a scheme with common areas or services are best sold freehold with rent charges in order to avoid enfranchisement, which can occur with leasehold tenure.

2.3. Type and Age

Most report forms have a section at the beginning for a brief description of the property. The valuer's aim in drafting this brief initial description should be to convey in a mere seven or eight words a pen-picture of the property which will enable, the building society manager, head office staff or solicitor to have immediately a fairly clear and accurate impression of the property which is the subject of the mortgage application.

This brief description can conveniently include:

The Number of Bedrooms.

The Style or Period—this will only be relevant in the cases of exceptional, or very old, houses. These are quite likely to be listed buildings and might include:

Medieval.
Half-timbered.
Tudor.
Elizabethan.
Georgian.
Regency.
Victorian Gothic.
Art Nouveau.
1930's modern movement, etc.

Any properties which date from these periods are likely to provide a welcome diversion for the valuer from the more usual run-of-the-mill estate type "semi".

Relationship with other Buildings.

Detached.
Semi-detached.
End-terraced (not quasi-semi).
Terraced.
Back-to-back.

In the case of a flat, the floor on which it is situated and the total number of floors in the block.

The Type of Property. This might include:-

Mansion.
Country house.
Manor house.
Farm house.
House.
Dormer bungalow.
Bungalow.
Maisonette.
Flat—self-contained or otherwise.
Shop with living accommodation.
Chalet.

Number of Storeys. The description can usefully be amplified by stating the number of storeys in cases where these exceed two.

Outbuildings and Grounds. Where appropriate the description can be extended by reference to "outbuildings/garage and grounds".

Former Use. Where the property has been converted from a former use this can be stated, e.g., where houses have been converted from formerly non-residential buildings such as barns, windmills, chapels, railway stations, etc., or a former toll house, Dissenting minister's house attached to a chapel, or caretaker's premises attached to industrial or commercial property.

So the final description might perhaps read "A six-bedroomed detached Victorian villa, outbuildings and grounds", or, more usually, "A three-bedroomed, semi-detached house and garage".

The age of the property, at least approximately, will often be known to the surveyor from his local knowledge. Occasionally there will be a date stone, especially on terraces. Enquiries from the vendor may elicit the information. Failing these, the valuer must turn to his own experience of styles and building construction techniques, looking for clues in such things as the general age of the neighbourhood, materials of construction, the plan arrangement, the elevational treatments, window proportions and disposition of glazing bars, and a lot of minor details which together should give the surveyor the evidence he needs to make a reasonably accurate assessment of the date of the property. Where properties have been substantially re-constructed, the original date and the date of the re-construction can both be given.

New houses can be described as "in course of erection" or "to be erected".

2.4. Construction

The descriptive section of the report should make reference to the method of construction of the property. It is normally best to do this under the sub-headings of foundations, walls, floors and roof.

Foundations. The surveyor will only know the type of foundations where he has local knowledge, or in the case of a new building. Types of foundation include:

Brick or stone footings only.
Concrete strip.
Trench-filled concrete.
Re-inforced concrete strip.
Piles (bored or driven) and ground beams.
Piers and ground beams.
Concrete raft.

Walls. The report should state whether the walls are solid or of cavity construction, and may give thicknesses. Where cavities have been filled with an insulating material, this is worth a mention. The wall can be described by reference to its materials and surface finish: sometimes the two leaves of a cavity wall will be in different materials and quite often stone facings will have a brickwork backing.

Stone walls. The stone may be specified, for example:

sandstone,
limestone,
granite,
flint,
slate,
Bath stone,
Portland stone,
etc.

Mention may be made of the class of stonework:

Rubble—flint; random rubble set dry; random rubble set in mortar; Kentish rag; random rubble built in courses; uncoursed, squared or snecked rubble; squared rubble built up to courses; regular coursed rubble.

Ashlar—Ashlar facings with brick backing or with rubble backing.

Brick. Brickwork can be described by reference to the type of brick, colour and bond. In a building society report it is usual to do no more than refer to the type of facings, for example:

London stock,
rustic/wire-cut/sand-faced/hand-made/red Accrington,
clay commons,
sandlime bricks,
concrete bricks.

Cob. Dried mud, local to the South-West (Devon).

Concrete Blocks. These are usual for the inner leaves of cavity walls in newer houses, where they are used in order to achieve the insulation required by the Building Regulations. They can also be used in the external leaf as a base for rendering, pebble-dashing or tile hanging. In addition there are fair-faced blocks, e.g. Forticrete, designed for external facing use and available in a variety of finishes.

Artificial Stone. This is in fact a type of concrete block. It is often used in areas where the Planning Authority require a stone finish and natural stone is too expensive.

In situ concrete. Occasionally found in flats and, with rendered finish, in Wimpey "no-fines" houses.

Pre-cast Concrete. Pre-cast wall units are sometimes found in system-built flats and also in factory-produced bungalows; often with an exposed aggregate finish.

Timber Frame. Timber framing is found in some kits imported from Canada and Scandinavia and also in some systems produced in the U.K. Frames can be one or two storeys in height and can easily be missed, as they are often clad with a brick skin.

Timber Finishes. Claddings of cedar shingles are found occasionally and in some areas the local vernacular includes weather-boarding. Occasionally the surveyor might meet a chalet of Scandinavian log construction.

Tile or Slate Hanging. Sometimes tile or slate hanging is applied to brickwork or stonework to prevent damp penetration. Sometimes it is fixed as a finish to timber framing or to blockwork when there should be a layer of sarking felt beneath it.

Rendering. This is sometimes applied to solid walls where

there has been a damp problem, or as a finish to blockwork or brickwork. There are various types, e.g.

Smooth cement rendering.
Stucco.
Pebble-dashing.
Tyrolean rendering (sprayed on).
Various textured finishes.

Rendering is often finished with a coat of cement paint. Sometimes it is lined or painted to imitate stonework.

Other Applied Finishes. Elevations can have applied finishes of stone cladding, tiles, etc.

Curtain Walling. Fully glazed wall areas with timber, galvanised steel or aluminium framing.

Steel or Concrete Framed Construction. This type of construction will normally only be found in blocks of flats. Concrete framing may be pre-cast or *in situ*. Occasionally steel framing is found in houses. There is further discussion on the problems of non-standard construction in Chapter 9.3. High alumina cement concrete is discussed in Chapter 8.2.

Floors. These may be described by reference to type and materials.

Solid Ground Floors. These include:

Concrete.
Flagstone.
Asphalt on concrete (or on flag).
Tiles (e.g. quarries) on concrete.
Woodblock or strip on concrete.

Suspended Ground Floors. There are two basic types:

(1) Pre-1965 Building Regulations timber floor with sub-floor space often taken down to foundation level and with earth or concrete sub-floor surface.
(2) Post-1965 Building Regulations timber floor with concrete sub-floor surface raised above the level of the external ground and with nominal void only.

In some areas ground floors above basements are constructed of flags supported on timber joists. Floors above basements are also sometimes of brick arch or vaulted construction. The most usual construction for suspended ground floors is timber joists with softwood boards, hardwood boards (oak, maple, beech, etc.) or chipboard.

Suspended Upper Floors. Construction may be:

Concrete, *in situ* with power-floated finish or screed.
Concrete filler joist construction.
Concrete, pre-cast with screed.
Concrete pre-cast beams or planks with filler posts or blocks between.
Timber joists with softwood boards, hardwood boards or chipboard, occasionally overlaid with parquetry.

Roofs. These can be described by reference to type, construction and materials.
Pitched Roofs (with or without parapets):

gabled,
hipped,
mono-pitched,
Mansard (true or imitation—with or without dormers).

Construction of Pitched Roofs:

purlins and rafters spanning between gables and cross walls,
ditto spanning between timber or steel trusses,
trussed rafters, bolted or gang-nailed.

Coverings of Pitched Roofs:

blue slate (usually from North Wales),
green slate (usually from Westmorland),
plain clay tiles,
clay pantiles,
plain concrete tiles,
inter-locking concrete tiles,
asbestos tiles.

(Slates and tiles normally have roofing felt beneath them or plaster torching on their undersides.)

boarding with lead, copper, zinc, asphalt or built-up felt finish,
woodwool slabs or straw board with asphalt or built-up felt finish,
asbestos sheeting,
metal decking or galvanised sheeting,
thatch.

Construction of Flat Roofs:

Concrete—*in situ,*
Concrete—pre-cast (with or without pots between beams),
timber joists spanning between walls,
timber joists spanning between steel beams or between
laminated or built-up ply-faced timber beams.

Finishes to Flat Roofs:

on concrete—asphalt or built-up felt,
on joists—boarding, woodwool slabs, chipboard, straw
board or plywood, with asphalt or built-up felt finish,
on joists—boarding with lead, copper or zinc finish.

Flat roofs are best laid with slight falls to get the water off
them.
Other Roofs:

vaulted roofs,
domed roofs.

In addition to modern books of building construction, any
valuer who has the opportunity to acquire copies of one of the
early editions of Mitchell's "Building Construction" and
"Advanced Building Construction" should do so—they contain a wealth of information on traditional building construction.

2.5. Accommodation

The major part of the descriptive section of the report consists
of a schedule of the accommodation in the property. This
should be listed floor by floor.

Some societies ask for room dimensions, others do not. In the
present writer's opinion there is little to be gained by giving
room sizes. The valuer will be measuring the external dimensions of the property, for the purposes of his plan and insurance valuation and thus will be aware of the total area which
may be relevant to his valuation. Measuring all the rooms is a
time-consuming occupation (although it may be possible to
transcribe the dimensions from the estate agent's handout) and
the valuer who dutifully measures each room is no more likely
to get his valuation or recommendation right than the valuer
who does not.

Those building society valuers who also practise estate

agency, and many do, will have their handy word-list of superlatives. These are surplus to requirements so far as the building society report is concerned: it is the basic facts that need recording, that is all.

In cases where dimensions are not required, it is worth recording how many of the bedrooms are double, and how many single. Some valuers have cast doubts on the suitability of one-bedroomed properties for mortgage but one-bedroom flats are in fact quite common in some areas, and there is often a real demand for them, as starter homes or for single people. There is no reason in principle why they should not be mortgageable.

Where a property is adapted to incorporate a "granny flat" this should be mentioned and is no drawback provided the self-contained section is not let on a formal tenancy.

The headroom only needs recording when it falls below the Building Regulation minimum of 2.3 m (7' 6¾").

Some rooms do not have any ventilation to the outside, either because there is no opening window or because an extension has been built across the original window: where this is the case it should be recorded.

2.6. Finishes and Fittings

Special wall, floor and ceiling finishes can best be referred to in the schedule of accommodation. Standard finishes do not need any mention but such features as wall panelling, extensive wall tiling, and decorative plaster ceilings are worthy of note.

Fixtures and fittings can also most conveniently be listed in the schedule of accommodation. These will include fireplaces, built-in cupboards, fitted wardrobes and other fitted furniture: most important are the sanitary and kitchen fittings. The sanitary fittings need a brief description but there is no need to go into great detail. It is important to indicate whether the fittings are of a modern standard or not. In the case of most modern houses the description, "bathroom with three-piece modern suite" will be quite adequate; or "bathroom with modern bath, pedestal washbasin, W.C., bidet and shower unit"; or "bathroom with old-fashioned W.C. and washbasin fittings".

Kitchen fittings can vary from a single stoneware sink to a fully-fitted kitchen incorporating many thousands of pound's worth of units of the highest quality. It is not necessary to enumerate all the units; a fully-fitted modern kitchen can adequately be described as "fully-fitted kitchen with double sink, waste disposal unit, hob unit and hood, double oven unit, extensive worktops, base units, wall cupboards, breakfast bar, etc., all of the highest modern standards". On the other hand one might merely have "kitchen with enamelled sink unit and limited wall cupboards only".

Defects affecting fixtures and fittings are best referred to in the surveyor's observations rather than under the schedule of accommodation, especially if they are to be the subject of a retention or undertaking. Where basic fittings are not operational, such as when a W.C. or washbasin is badly cracked, it should be a condition of mortgage that they are replaced.

2.7. Out-buildings and Grounds

The out-buildings and grounds should be listed in similar manner to the accommodation.

Out-buildings include garages, coach houses, stables, barns, loose boxes, garden sheds, store rooms, coal sheds, outside toilets, workshops, greenhouses, potting sheds, conservatories, orangeries, dovecotes, pig sties, hen cabins, summer houses, loggias, swimming pools, tennis pavilions and courts, gate-houses, water towers, staff cottages, etc. They should be listed with brief descriptive notes, drawing attention to any special features or problem areas, such as dilapidated condition.

The provisions for cars are especially important and often have a significant effect on value. Specific reference should always be made to parking and garage facilities, and where there is a garage, its construction and condition should be noted. Provisions for cars will range through the following list.

No parking space within the curtilage or near by.

No parking space within the curtilage but parking permitted on the adjacent road.

Parking space for one car within the curtilage but no garage space.

Space available for the erection of a garage within the curtilage, subject to planning permission.

Car port for one car.

Garage on near-by colony included in the sale.

Garage on near-by plot but held on annual tenancy only (and thus excluded from the mortgage security).

Single timber/asbestos garage.

Single brick garage.

Double brick garage.

Garage accomodation for .... cars.

Staff accommodation can sometimes give rise to problems in getting vacant possession. A former staff flat or cottage integral with or attached to the main house but which has been let off on a normal tenancy will almost certainly have to be bought complete with its tenant and in most cases the presence of a tenanted unit on the doorstep will detract from the main house and appreciably lower its value.

Grounds. If the front door of the property opens directly on to the street this should be noted; or if the front garden is particularly small. Where gardens are extensive, an approximate acreage should be given with a brief description of the land, e.g. "grounds extending to 2 acres and comprising cultivated garden in the proximity of the house, the remainder being a fenced paddock". Where the land has features which could be onerous, these should be noted, e.g. steep slopes, retaining walls, unfenced areas, river banks, marshy ground, overgrown or uncultivated areas, unpaved drives, etc. On the positive side, mature trees, well stocked and cultivated gardens, paved terraces and patios, internal garden courts, etc., are worthy of mention. Land with development potential should be mentioned, especially if planning permission exists.

Attention required to fences, drives, land drainage, etc., is best referred to in the valuer's observations, where attention can also be drawn to any specific problem areas, such as badly bulging retaining walls or trees too near to the house.

2.8. Location

The location of a property is a vital factor so far as its valuation is concerned. Two very similar houses situated a mere couple of miles apart may have totally different market values.

Types of area range from first-class residential, through good residential, average residential, poor residential, to mixed residential/industrial or residential/commercial. Areas may be urban, suburban, rural village, or a property may be in an isolated rural situation.

There is a tendency for areas to improve as one moves away from the centres of towns, but there are many exceptions to this trend.

Prices are obviously higher in an area of high demand,

especially the south-east of England, and in areas of high employment. Conversely, prices tend to be lower where there is high unemployment. An artificial situation can be created in an area where there is a demand for holiday or second homes.

Some areas are improving and the evidence will be seen in modernised properties, conversions, an increasing air of prosperity and perhaps designation as a general improvement area. Other areas are declining, especially in urban districts. Signs of decline include conversion of mainly 19th century houses into flats and "bed-sits," properties in multiple occupation, houses being used for secondary commercial purposes, properties not being maintained properly and consequently acquiring a rather dilapidated air, unkempt gardens, litter, loose mongrel dogs, graffiti, etc. Once deterioration of an area has commenced it can be quite rapid. Larger properties tend to be bought at fairly low prices by purchasers who cannot afford to maintain or run them. Once an area has started to decline like this, a building society valuer is bound to take a cautious approach and this in turn accentuates the problem. The valuer must always be looking ahead to try to assess what the area may be like towards the end of a mortgage term of perhaps 20 or 25 years. Inner urban areas which are run-down have so often in the recent past been subject to wholesale demolition and re-development, although perhaps not until sales of properties in the district have been blighted for some years. Whilst the provision of compensation at market value for owner-occupiers in houses which are compulsorily acquired is a welcome provision compared with the former site-value-only provision, getting the compensation in advance of the C.P.O. is not always straightforward. The current trend of rehabilitation of existing properties is much to be welcomed but even where this is to take place there can be uncertainties in so far that it is not uncommon for alternate rows of terraced houses to be demolished, to give more open space. In addition to housing re-development schemes, the surveyor will want to know if the property he is concerned with is in the route of a projected motorway or affected by some other development proposals. It is not only in inner urban areas that planning proposals can affect values; planning permission for development in the suburbs or villages can mean the loss of a magnificent outlook from an existing property, which may significantly reduce its value. If the proposed development happens to be a large council housing estate the loss in value may be more drastic.

Nor are the suburbs and country exempt from motorway construction and sewage works.

Social and economic changes have, in many places, brought about the decline of isolated rural and coastal communities. In some areas remote and inaccessible smallholdings and cottages have become derelict. The risks of this happening are much higher where there is no adequate vehicular access, for example, island properties. Where an isolated community is almost entirely dependant on one source of employment such as a local factory, mine or quarry, and this source of employment closes down, it can lead to a complete village becoming derelict. A classic example of this is Porth-y-nant on the Lleyn peninsular of North Wales. This village, reached only by sea, horse or on foot, was originally a farming community but much extended in the 19th century to serve local quarries. Bounded by sea and cliffs it is now completely deserted. The valuer must attempt to look ahead for the full term of the proposed mortgage and try to assess whether or not rural de-population or the economic decline of a traditional local industry may affect property values, and to take this into account in his recommendation.

Some districts are favoured by particular ethnic or religious groups and this can have a marked effect on values. Thus there may be a high demand by Jewish purchasers for properties within a short distance of an existing synagogue.

The valuer must always be on the look-out for near-by property or activities which will reduce the value of the house he is surveying. This may be no more than the run-down condition of the adjoining house, perhaps because it is occupied by an elderly recluse. Noise can be a problem, caused either by a very busy road, or the flight path of aircraft, or an adjoining factory or a children's playground in the immediate vicinity. Pubs and clubs can be a nuisance late at night, as can all-night cafés. Values are likely to be affected in the immediate vicinity of public lavatories, bus shelters of the type where teenagers congregate, betting shops, fish and chip shops, pet shops, butchers and/or tripe shops, slaughter houses, knackers yards, fellmongeries, tanneries, animal bye-products factories, some chemical factories, especially those using dangerous or unpleasant-smelling chemicals, nuclear installations, prisons, detention centres, probation hostels, mental hospitals and hostels, chapels of rest, cemeteries, certain types of shops, sewage works, middens, pig farms, broiler houses, buildings used by some minority religious or political groups, etc.

On the other hand there are positive amenities which are likely to increase values if they are available and reduce them if not. These include shops, primary schools, secondary schools parks/open spaces/play areas, community activities such as facilities for young people (e.g. youth clubs, uniformed organisations) and to a lesser extent sports facilities—tennis/squash/swimming/riding/golf clubs, etc.; provision for cultural activities and churches.

Accessibility is very important, ranging from being within commuting distance of London or some other centre, to not too steep a hill to push the pram up. The availability and frequency of public transport can be very important. Proximity to an access point to the motorway network will be a consideration to many people whose jobs involve travel, and at the top end of the market reasonable proximity to an airport may be considered essential. The building of a new motorway or bridge may cause a marked change in property prices in the affected area. A typical example is provided by Rossendale in East Lancashire, traditionally a textile manufacturing area which has suffered serious economic decline since the last war but where new life and increasing property prices have been brought about by the M66 motorway, opened in 1978, and bringing the area within easy commuting distance of Manchester.

2.9. Light and Power

The valuer will need to record the services which are laid on to the property, or easily available, and the means of heating.

Gas may be laid on, or available if required. Sometimes gas is laid on but the supply pipe is not of sufficient size for a central heating installation: however, investigation at this depth is beyond the scope of a building society survey. Where gas is not available, especially in larger rural properties, one occasionally finds large propane gas tanks which are replenished from time to time by tanker.

Electricity is available in most properties nowadays. Where there is no mains electricity there may be a petrol or diesel-driven generator, but it is unlikely that a property without mains electricity will be suitable for normal mortgage advance.

Lighting will usually be electric. Properties reliant on mains gas, Calor gas or paraffin for lighting are few and far between.

Electric power sockets may be of the 5 amp two-pin type or 13 or 15 amp three-pin traditional Wylex, or the round pin type or of the modern type with square pins. Normally socket outlets of the square pin type will be on a ring main system which conforms to modern standards. If a property still has traditional Wylex or round pin plugs it is almost certain that re-wiring is necessary and a retention should be made until it has been done, together with the consequential decoration. The surveyor needs to be aware of the common practice of just renewing the socket outlets and switches themselves, leaving the old wiring. A clue to the real state of the wiring can often be gleaned by the state of the lighting drops in the bedrooms, or by looking at the wiring at the distribution board. If there are cast-iron switch boxes and porcelain fuses it is likely that re-wiring will be necessary. If in doubt the surveyor can recommend that the applicant obtains an electrical engineer's report and carries out such work as is recommended, with an undertaking being required by the society that this will be done or a retention made in the sum of the estimates obtained. Any wiring that is over about 25 years old must be considered suspect.

The mode of space-heating must be recorded on the report and will affect the valuation. Gas-fired central heating is currently considered by many people to be the cleanest and most economical, followed by oil-fired central heating. The least satisfactory situation is where there are no fireplaces or fixed heating appliances at all, merely a reliance on portable electric fires or even Calor gas or paraffin stoves.

The space-heating systems likely to be encountered will include:

open fires,
open fires with "all-night" burners,
open fires of Baxi type,
solid fuel stoves,
wood-burning stoves,
individual gas fires,
individual fixed electric heaters or radiators,
portable electric heaters,
Calor gas stoves,
paraffin stoves,
electric under-floor heating,
electric ceiling heating,
electric storage heaters,
electric warm-air central heating,
solid fuel central heating,
oil-fired central heating,
oil-fired warm-air heating,

gas-fired central heating,
gas-fired warm-air heating.

It may be appropriate to mention the type of fireplace or appliance, and whether a central heating system has thermostat and clock controls. Where the system is only partial, this should be noted. Gas systems may run on mains gas or locally stored gas.

Oil tanks can prove difficult if they spring a leak and a badly rusted tank needs attention.

Properties with open fires need provision for storage of fuel.

Pipework may be micro-bore, which in some parts of the country may be prone to furring-up, small-bore copper or steel alloy, medium-bore mild steel or the old large-bore cast iron. Most systems of the latter type are likely to be due for renewal. Radiators may be traditional cast iron, modern pressed steel, skirting heaters or fan assisted radiators.

In a rising number of cases the surveyor will come across solar heating panels, normally in the roof and designed to provide a proportion of the space heating, or more usually water heating.

The valuer should record the type of water heating and draw attention to any major defect or obsolescence in it.

Water heating may be by:

back boiler behind an open fire,
solid fuel boiler,
the central heating boiler, of whatever fuel,
a gas water-heater near the cylinder,
an electric immersion heater,
individual gas-heaters over sink and washbasin,
individual electric heaters over sink and washbasin.

Solar heating may supplement any of the above but is unlikely to be adequate on its own.

Insulation will give economies in running costs. Apart from insulation built in during construction, such as thermal insulating block walls or rigid polystyrene sheets built into the cavity, insulation can be fairly easily increased by means of

—the insulation of the roof voids, either by a fibreglass quilt (desirable minimum thickness 3″) or by granules,
—double glazing either by sealed units or by subsidiary internal windows, preferably of the aluminium-framed sliding type,

—cavity fill insulation either with expanded polyurethane foam or with mineral fibre (always provided the property is not in an exposed position),

—insulation of pipe runs in sub-floor and ceiling spaces: also where pipes pass through outbuildings which do not need heat.

—insulation of hot water cylinder.

If the valuer comes across anything which is an obvious fire risk, such as inflammable material stored immediately next to or on top of a boiler, or where a boiler is found in a confined space with no proper ventilation, he may consider it prudent to report it.

Communications play an increasing part in modern life. In some areas the presence of a telephone in a property may be a positive selling point, for example in remote properties where the installation of a telephone could be a major undertaking or in telephone exchange areas where there is a shortage of lines and hence a waiting list for new phones.

There is radio and television coverage of the whole country, but some properties situated in the bottoms of steep valleys may not enjoy satisfactory television reception, or at least not without high aerial towers. With the widespread popularity of television, the fact that a property could not receive it would be likely to limit the number of prospective purchasers.

2.10. Water Supply

The vast majority of houses enjoy a water supply from the Water Authority mains in the adjoining street. A turn of the tap over the kitchen sink, which is normally taken directly off the mains for drinking water purposes, will confirm that pressure is adequate and the surveyor need concern himself no further on this point.

It is when there is no mains water or when the property does not front a highway in which the water main is laid that the problems occur and the valuer needs to be very much on his guard. Where a property relies on spring or well water from a source within its own curtilage, the valuer will want to take a look at the spring or well to ascertain its general condition and also to inspect the pumping and storage arrangements. Most properties that still rely on spring or well water nowadays will have electric pumps controlled by float switches, raising the water to storage tanks. Where there is still reliance on hand-

pumping the valuer will wish to make it a condition of
mortgage that electric pumping facilities and proper water
storage are introduced. In cases where there is reliance on
spring or well water the valuer will need to be able to assure
the building society that the property is going to enjoy a
suitable and sufficient water supply for the whole of the term of
the mortgage, which may be as long as 25 years. If the water
supply fails, the property becomes unsaleable. For this reason
the surveyor cannot afford to take risks, and it is suggested that
it is not adequate to rely on verbal assurances but to make any
mortgage advance subject to documentary evidence being
produced. This evidence should cover the adequacy of the
supply by way of a suitably qualified engineer's report and/or
affidavits from persons who have known the property over a
very long period of time and who can state that the supply has
not been known to dry up during living memory. Assurances
will also be required about the quality of the water by way of a
report from a qualified analyst or from the local Environmental
Health Department. An alternative would be a written statement from the Water Authority to the effect that mains water is
available on request and giving an estimated cost for laying the
main; in which case, if there are doubts about the spring or well
supply a retention in the sum of the Water Authority's estimate
should be made.

Where a property has mains water but is not adjacent to the
highway in which the Water Authority main is situated, or
where it draws water from a well or spring which is not
situated within the curtilage of the property, the valuer will
be concerned that any easements for pipes passing through
land in other ownerships are in order. Where water has to be
pumped from the main to the property the valuer will also
want to ensure that the necessary easement exists for the
pumping chamber and power cable to it. Where a spring or
well is on land in another ownership, water rights must be in
order so that an adjoining owner can be prevented from doing
anything which might contaminate the supply, and there will
need to be easements for any cisterns, electric or wind pumps
or rams.

The valuer cannot check these easements himself but he
should make specific reference in his report to any wells,
springs, equipment, cables or pipes which apparently are
situated on land in the ownership of another party. These items
should also be indicated on the block plan and it is then up to
the Society's solicitor to ascertain that the easements are in

order. When considering an estimate from a Water Authority for the provision of mains water to a property, the surveyor must also take into consideration any problems raised by the need for easements. Where private water facilities are shared between two or more properties, this should also be noted so that the solicitor is aware of the situation.

Sometimes private water supply facilities will be found to be in need of major overhaul or repairs and in such cases the valuer will usually make a retention in the sum of an estimate to be obtained from a suitable contractor. Where the valuer anticipates that future maintenance of a private water supply system may be onerous, he may consider it wise to limit the percentage advance recommended.

In cases where suitable assurances as to the future sufficiency and quality of the water supply cannot be obtained, the valuer has no option but to advise against taking the property into mortgage.

In the unlikely event of the valuer coming across a property which still relies on a public pump or water cart the property must be considered unsuitable for mortgage.

Where mains supply is available but for some reason not laid on, or where it is laid on but pressure is totally inadequate, then an advance will be recommended subject to a retention in the sum of an estimate to be obtained from the Water Authority for doing the necessary work.

Pipework, cold water tanks and hot water cylinders will merit a mention only if they are in need of renewal, as in the cases of badly sagging lead pipework, pipes which are furred up, rusted water tanks or cylinders which are corroded around their fittings.

Where a property has a water supply it is to be anticipated that it will also have a means of heating the water, either by back boiler, immersion heater, gas heater, solid fuel stove or central heating boiler. It is only if a property has no provision for hot water that a valuer will wish to comment and to cover this by means of a retention.

2.11. Drainage and Sanitation

An important task is to ascertain whether or not the property enjoys the benefits of main drainage. This drainage may be:

A Combined System. In this case there is one drain carrying surface water and foul with either a direct connection to a public sewer in the adjacent street or a connection into a private drain serving several houses, with reciprocal rights to use the drain and shared responsibilities for its maintenance, or;

A Dual System. This involves separate drains for foul and surface water with the foul drain connected directly to the public sewer in the adjacent street or into a private drain serving several houses with reciprocal rights to use the drain and shared responsibilities for its maintenance; and the surface water connected into a public surface water sewer, or into the last manhole on the foul drainage system or to a water course or soak-away, either directly or via a private drain serving two or more properties, with shared responsibilities for its maintenance.

Pumped Sewage. Sometimes the invert level of the drains to a dwelling is below the public sewer, necessitating a sewage pump, serving one property or several. As the maintenance of a sewage pump can be very onerous it is important for the surveyor to ascertain whether it has been adopted by the Local Authority or not and if not (as is usually the case) what condition the pump is in and who is responsible for routine servicing and the more major repairs which become necessary from time to time.

Secondary float-operated pumps may also be found serving small collecting sumps in basements which are below drain level, but these are not in the same league, so far as potential problems are concerned, as true sewage pumps.

Pumped systems need treating with some caution and may have the effect of reducing the percentage advance recommended. Otherwise, if there is main drainage and no visual evidence of blockage the surveyor need concern himself no further with the drains, other than to note any obvious easements where the drains cross another owner's land (apart from the normal arrangement on a housing estate). Blockages tend to show by the drain backing up and spilling out at the edges of manhole covers or at gullies. Where this is noticed any advance recommended should be subject to a drain test being made and any work found to be necessary being carried out, probably with an appropriate retention being held from the advance.

Where there is no main drainage the valuer will generally encounter:

Septic Tank Drainage. The tank may either serve one property or several and can be of traditional design with brick or concrete construction or of the more modern pre-cast concrete or fibre-glass manufacture. From time to time tanks need cleaning out and renewing of filter media. Occasionally the fabric of the tank will be in a poor state, perhaps even to the extent of a new tank being necessary. Surface water is not usually put through the tank but discharges direct to a water course or field drain system or soak-away. The effluent from the septic tank may have to be pumped to raise it from the tank outlet to a height which will enable it to be got away without making the area around the tank waterlogged. Septic tanks are quite acceptable in principle, providing they are in good order. If they have an offensive smell they almost certainly are in need of overhaul and this should be a condition of mortgage. Sometimes septic tanks are sited on another owner's land and where this is the case it should be shown on the surveyor's plan, with drain runs, etc., so that the solicitor can confirm that the necessary easements are in order. The responsibilities for maintenance should also be determined.

Drainage to a Private Sewage Works. This is rare but does occur in some rural areas, especially where properties were originally part of a landed estate, or on newer housing estates in cases where the public sewer is overloaded. The condition of the plant should be noted and responsibilities for maintenance determined. In these cases the surface water will usually be drained separately.

Drainage to a Cesspit. This may serve either one property or several. It is usual where there is no main drainage and where the site is unsuitable for a septic tank, either because of the lie of the land or because there is insufficient land available within the curtilage of the property. The valuer will need to determine the condition of the tank and find out who is responsible for emptying and cleaning it, how often this has to be done and what costs are involved. In some cases the Local Authority will empty the tank without charge. Surface water will normally discharge elsewhere. Cesspits are far from ideal and will certainly affect the value of a property. Whether a property with cesspit drainage is suitable security for a mortgage advance will tend to depend upon local attitudes to this type of arrangement and the surveyor will have to exercise his judgment. If the cesspit is situated on land in someone else's ownership, this fact should be noted on the plan.

Chemical Closets. These are normally only found where there is no main sewer available and no facility for installing a septic tank. If it is possible to connect into a sewer or to install a septic tank, the mortgage should be conditional upon this being done (probably with a further advance being granted to assist with the work). Where this is not practical the property will almost certainly be unsuitable for mortgage advance, especially as it is not normal for a Local Authority to give an improvement grant on a property where a water closet cannot be provided and there must be a risk that the house will be declared "unfit for human habitation", with a consequent clearance, demolition or closing order being made.

Earth Closets. Nowadays these are usually found only in remote rural areas.

In some properties there will be a water closet which is not accessible from within the dwelling. In these cases the valuer must assess if a w.c. compartment (and perhaps even a full bathroom) can be introduced within the property, or by building on a small extension. Where this can be done it should be made a condition of mortgage (with perhaps a further advance being recommended towards the cost of the work) but where it is impractical to install an internal water closet the property is probably unsuitable for mortgage advance.

If the w.c. compartment is unventilated or opens directly off the kitchen or if the pedestal itself is of an old-fashioned type, cracked or badly marked, the provision of ventilation and/or replacement of the pedestal should be made conditions of mortgage.

On new developments, the Local Authority may issue a Private Sewer Order under Section 38 of the Public Health Act 1936, requiring several houses to be drained in combination by means of a private sewer, up to the point where it meets the public sewer. The costs of maintaining any repairing and such private sewer are borne jointly by the owners of the properties served by it.

The main sewers on new developments will generally be laid beneath the roads. Most new estates will have a dual system of drainage with separate sewers for foul sewerage and surface water, although the surface water may in fact be connected to the last manhole on the foul system where there is no other suitable place for it to discharge. Occasionally some of the surface water may go to soak-aways, in which case the valuer should be on the lookout for waterlogged ground.

It is of considerable importance to the purchasers of new properties, and to the mortgagees, that main sewers on new developments are adopted by the Local Authority. If this is not done the property owners will be responsible for maintaining the sewers. It is particularly desirable from the point of view of purchasers that the Local Authority should adopt any sewage pumps or local treatment pumps, but often authorities will not accept these, understandably in view of the fairly onerous maintenance requirements. A developer has two options open to him so far as adoption of sewage works and sewers is concerned. These are:

(1) The sewers, etc., may be constructed and then application made to the Local Authority requesting them to make a declaration vesting the sewers in the authority under Section 17(2) of the Public Health Act 1936. The Local Authority and, on an appeal, the Minister, in deciding whether a declaration should be made, shall have regard to all the circumstances and in particular to the following considerations:

(a) Whether the sewer or works in question is or are adapted to, or required for, any general system of sewerage or sewage disposal which the Authority have provided, or propose to provide, for their district or any part thereof;

(b) Whether the sewer is constructed under a highway, or under land reserved by a planning scheme for a street;

(c) The number of buildings which the sewer is intended to serve, and whether, regard being had to the proximity of other buildings or the prospect of future development, it is likely to be required to serve additional buildings;

(d) The method of construction and the state of repair of the sewer or works; and

(e) In the case where an owner objects, whether the making of the proposed declaration will be seriously detrimental to him.

(2) Under Section 18(1) of the Public Health Act 1936 a developer may agree with the Local Authority, prior to construction of the sewer or sewerage works, that if the sewer or works is or are constructed in accordance with the terms of the

agreement, the Local Authority will upon the completion of the work, declare the sewer or works to be vested in them.

The responsibility for sewers rests with the regional Water Authority but it is normal practice for Local Authorities to act as agents for water authorities. If a developer adopts the Section 17 approach, there could be considerable problems for purchasers and mortgagees as the Authority may decline to adopt the sewers, or may decline to accept them without extensive testing at the applicant's expense—it is understood that in one area a water authority has insisted on television inspection of all sewers to be adopted under Section 17. The Section 18 method gives useful safeguards to purchasers and mortgagees as the Authority inspects the sewers as they are laid and is this bound to accept them on completion. However, in some areas the authorities make considerable charges for inspecting the sewers whilst they are being laid (it is understood that these charges may amount to as much as between 5% and 8% of the total construction costs of the sewers) and this has tended to encourage some developers to adopt the Section 17 procedure.

In order to safeguard the security of the Society so far as the sewerage of properties on new estates is concerned, it is necessary to ensure that there is a Section 18 agreement in being and also, no later than the final inspection of a new house, that all the main sewers and any sewage works serving it are complete, or substantially complete, and connected up.

So far as surface water drainage is concerned, a possible problem is the backing up of the drain causing flooding, possibly due to the water level in the stream or dyke into which the drain discharges rising up above the point of discharge after heavy rain. Flooding sometimes also occurs when near-by streams burst their banks or in coastal properties when there are exceptionally high tides. Local knowledge is generally the best guide to properties affected by these problems although the proximity of a stream, river or the sea should always make a valuer suspicious. Where a property is subject to regular flooding, albeit infrequently, it is unlikely to provide suitable security for mortgage advance.

2.12. Easements and Rights

An easement is a right capable of forming the subject-matter of a grant which is appurtenant to the land of one person and exercisable over the land of another.

Where there is an easement which may affect the value or security of the property being surveyed, the valuer should make reference to it. The most common easements which will fall into this category will be rights of way. These may benefit the property being surveyed, such as a right of way over an adjoining owner's land, or the right to lay and maintain pipes or cables over that land; or they may be a burden to the property being surveyed, such as rights of way of adjoining owners across the property.

Similarly the property may be a subject to a public right, e.g., a public footpath across it.

In some cases there will be reciprocal rights whereby adjoining owners will have common use of a driveway or yard, court or garden. Where there is a common drainage system or houses are supplied with fuel oil from a central tank, there will be reciprocal rights in respect of drains and oil supply lines. Reciprocal rights in respect of common parts of flats are discussed in Chapter 8.

The following rights have been held to be easements:

The use of a letter-box, a lavatory and a kitchen.
The use of a wall for fixing a sign or for supporting a creeper.
The use of coal sheds and the storage of trade materials on the servient tenement.

Besides easements, a property may enjoy rights of common such as the common of pasture, whereby an owner of cattle has the right with others to pasture his cattle on another's land.

Sometimes there are easements allowing gas or water mains or electricity cables to be laid through the grounds of a property, or for electric cables to cross the land overhead, in which case there may be a small rent receivable.

Where a new property or extension is to be built, the valuer should satisfy himself that the existing rights of light of adjoining or near-by owners are not going to be interfered with. There is no legal formula to apply in connection with rights of light and each case must be taken on its merits, nevertheless as a rough rule of thumb it is likely that a right of light will be interfered with if a line drawn at 45° from the cill of an existing window is bisected by a new building.

If there is a culvert beneath the site of the property being surveyed, considerable caution should be exercised. Not only is there a risk of possible structural movement to the property in the event of collapse of the culvert, but in some cases the responsibility for the maintenance of the culvert will fall upon the owner of the land beneath which it runs, as the following example of an actual case illustrates.

Example

Some 20 years after a building was built the owners were served with notice by the Local Authority requiring them to repair a culvert which was near to collapse and which ran some 12 m beneath the site (although the nearest access point was some distance away and the water rights on the stream running through the culvert were enjoyed by others). The estimated costs of repair amounted to several thousand pounds.

2.13. Roads and Road Charges

Questions relating to roads tend to be framed in the following terms on building society report forms.

"Are the roads fronting the property maintainable at public expense?"

"Estimated cost of completing roadworks?"

"Are there any outstanding paving charges relating to this property?"

The point behind these questions is that if an unmade road is paved by the Local Authority the costs of paving the road will be apportioned between the properties fronting on to the road. The sums involved can be substantial, amounting in the case of, say, a street alongside the gable wall of an end-terraced house to perhaps as much as 25% of the market value of the house. If a property where street works are being carried out comes into the possession of the society, the society will find itself responsible for the cost of the street works and hence the security of the property is impaired.

Where roads adjoining a property are not made up, many societies ask for an estimate of the costs of making them up. This is calculated by taking off approximate quantities for the area of roadwork involved and pricing them out. In practice this is not done on each occasion and, once typical costs per square metre have been calculated by means of approximate quantities, the surveyor will probably apply the resultant figure per square metre in each case, adjusting as appropriate. It is important to bear in mind that a frontager is only responsible for the costs of paving up to the centre line of the road.

Sometimes, mainly on new estates, the roads will be partially made up, and then appropriately reduced figures will be used by the valuer in calculating the cost of outstanding roadworks.

When the estimated cost of completing the roadworks is determined, the surveyor must decide, firstly, if he should reduce the valuation. This will only be appropriate where private street works are imminent or where there are outstanding payments due for recently completed roadworks—any such payments due will be a charge on the property and sometimes will only come to light when the solicitor makes his searches. Local knowledge obviously helps the surveyor in these matters, but whenever a recently made-up road fronting older properties is encountered, or an unmade road with several houses fronting on to it, then enquiries should be made to the Local Authority.

In cases where roadworks are not imminent but there is a possibility of them being carried out during the term of the mortgage, a retention is appropriate, in the sum of the estimated costs of the paving liability.

There will be some cases where the roads are not made-up but where neither devaluation nor a retention are appropriate. These cases are:

(1) Where the proposed purchase price clearly takes into account the road liability.

(2) Where the road is not likely to be made up during the term of the mortgage. The fact that the road is not listed in the Local Authority's "current proposals for private street works" is not sufficient of itself to make a retention inappropriate; it could well be that within a year or so the street will be found to be in the current proposals.

(3) Where the unmade road is an ancient highway. Here again local knowledge will be helpful to the surveyor, but if in doubt recommend a retention, which can always be waived if the solicitor produces appropriate information.

(4) In the case of new developments the costs of roadworks are likely to be included in the price of the house and the Local Authority will have required the developer either to make a payment equivalent to the estimated costs of the proposed roads under the Advance Payments Code, found in Section 192 of Part IX of the Highways Act 1959; or to have entered into an agreement to make up the roads under Section 40 of the same Act.

The Advance Payments Code is not applicable when there is already a Section 40 agreement. Furthermore a sum paid or secured under the Advance Payments Code may be released if a Section 40 agreement is subsequently entered into and the weakness with a Section 40 agreement can be that the agreement may be backed by no more than the bond of the developer himself or of a guarantor of less than major banker or insurance company standing. If this is the case the building society should be advised to make a retention in respect of roadworks, but where there is a Section 40 agreement backed by a full deposit of cash or the bond of a major bank or insurance company, no retention is necessary.

Access to some properties is over roads which are not maintainable at public expense. These may be either public rights of way or private drives. Unmade access tracks can be several miles long, serving several properties and with no proper arrangements for the apportionment of maintenance responsibility. Where such tracks are regularly used by heavy vehicles the problem can be acute and may be sufficiently severe to make the property unsuitable as security for mortgage.

Where unmade private drives are in poor state, a retention in the sum of the valuer's estimate of the costs of repair is appropriate. The condition of and maintenance responsibilities for unmade access roads and drives will affect the market value of the property.

Properties fronting a major road present a different problem. Here there may be a proposed road improvement line which will take the front garden and whilst some compensation will be payable it may not represent the full amount of the reduction in market value, especially during the eighteen months or so when the work is being carried out, with mud in winter and dust in summer. In a similar way the property may be sited near the line of a proposed motorway or new by-pass road which is likely to result in loss of value, arising from the inconvenience during construction and traffic noise afterwards. Even where no road improvements are planned, the road may be so busy that it is impossible to get a car out of a driveway or to cross the road at rush hour, or there may be existing or anticipated parking or unloading restrictions. These matters will all be reflected in the valuation of the property.

Example

Calculate liability for road charges for a property having a 10 m frontage to an unmade road 11 m wide, comprising 2 × 2 m footpaths and 7 m carriageway.

Note. Liability up to middle of road only. Calculation based on approximate quantities, using items as listed in Spon's

"Architects' and Builders' Price Book," and with Spon's rates adjusted to take inflation into account.

	£
Pavings to pavements 750 × 600 × 50 mm concrete flags, bedding in lime mortar, jointing and pointing in cement mortar, 6 mm joints straight both ways, ash filling and making up levels average 100 mm thick, excavating reduced levels average 150 mm deep.	20 sq.m at £7.40 148·00
Pavings to roads, to falls, cross falls or slopes not exceeding 15° from horizontal, 75 mm tarmacadam, hardcore filling 225 mm thick, pre-cast concrete 225 × 125 mm kerbs and channels both sides, *in situ* concrete mix 11.5N/ mm squared foundations, excavating to reduced levels not exceeding 300 mm deep, depositing in temporary spoil heaps, filling in making up levels, depositing and compacting in layers, carting away surplus.	35.0 sq.m at £9·70 339·50
Vitrified clay street gulley, outlet, salt glazed, cement mortar joint to vitrified clay pipe, bedding and surrounding in normal concrete mix 11.5 N/ mm squared 40 mm aggregate with cast iron road grating and frame, bedding and pointing in cement mortar, one course half brick thick wall in common bricks in cement mortar, pipe connection to sewer.	Say 50% of 1 at £150 75·00

Part cost of street lighting   Say 75·00

                                                   Total 637·50
Add for preliminaries at 15%   95·63

Add for consulting engineer's   733·13
fees at 10%   73·31
                                            Total cost 806·44

                                              Say £810·00

                              Average overall cost per sq.
                              metre = £14·72, say £15·00
                              Approx. cost per metre run of
                              frontage (*i.e.* half of road) =
                              £80·00

Chapter 3

Building Defects

3.1. Structural Movement of Foundations and Walls

Off all the defects which the building society valuer will meet, structural movement of the main fabric of a house or flat is the one likely to have the most serious consequences. It is also easily missed!

Few other defects are so far-reaching as sometimes to lead to the need to demolish a house completely. Most experienced valuers will know cases where this has happened, as well as cases where expensive under-pinning has been necessary, or where a house has been rendered virtually unsaleable. Nor are these problems limited to older properties. The N.H.B.C. has reported many cases of new houses where major work has been necessary and indeed where repairs were totaly uneconomic and the Council has in some cases compensated owners for the full cost of the property to enable them to purchase alternative new homes.

Whilst the 10 year N.H.B.C. certificate does give purchasers very valuable protection it should not be overlooked that second and subsequent purchasers will receive no assistance in respect of defects which could have been ascertained on survey at the time they purchased the property.

There are similar problems with the subsidence cover provided by most standard householders' insurance policies in that apart from the fact that the insured may be expected to pay an excess equal to 3% of the reinstatement value, the insurers often will not meet any of the costs of underpinning if the original foundations are shown to be inadequate in depth or size, nor will they meet claims for settlement which was apparent at the time the policy was effected.

The building society valuer is not a civil or structural engineer and only occasionally will he be an architect or chartered building surveyor. Nor is the building society valuer expected, or paid, to do a detailed structural investigation. Nevertheless he does need to be aware of the main causes of structural movement, the evidence of these, and the consequent implications, at least to the extent of the information available in such standard text-books as Melville & Gordon's "Structural Surveys of Dwelling Houses" and Eldridge's "Common Defects in Buildings."

The main causes of structural movement are:

Landslip. This is rare but a case came before the Courts in 1977 relating to an estate built on a hillside which moved due to a particular geological formation. All steeply sloping sites should be treated with some suspicion, and any evidence of movement of the property or of the land itself should be treated with the utmost caution, with the property either being turned down as unsuitable for mortgage if there is evidence of serious recent movement, or an advance being recommended conditional upon a satisfactory report from a suitably qualified structural or civil engineer.

Erosion. This, too, is rare but there are houses built at the top of seaside cliffs and steep river banks where sea or river are gradually getting nearer and nearer to the house. In the case of rivers this situation is not always as obvious as one might expect it to be!

Differential Settlement. All properties settle to some extent, apart from those built on rock. A problem occurs when one part of the house settles rather more than other parts. The evidence is to be seen in door and window frames being out of square, cracks in brickwork or stonework, walls out of plumb, floors out of level, disturbed roof coverings, especially at party walls, and cracking or stretching of wallpaper at the junction of walls and ceilings. The causes of differential settlement are many and include geological faults, soft or filled ground, foundations of inadequate size or depth, differing ground conditions under different parts of the property, different foundation depths for different parts of the building, unsuitable foundation design for steeply sloping sites, underground water courses or broken drains, clay shrinkage or underground workings. Often the evidence is no more than hairline cracks. It is not always easy to distinguish between superficial cracking of plasterwork or external rendering and genuine structural cracks. Sometimes attempts will have been made to hide the evidence by strategic positioning of furniture or re-decoration. Besides noting the evidence, the surveyor must assess whether or not it is recent. Have cracks opened since they were last pointed up or since the house was last decorated? Are the cracks fresh in colour or black with age like their surroundings?

If the movement is limited to an outbuilding, extension or bay, it is almost certain that its foundations do not go down to the depth of those of the main house. The condition of adjoining properties may give some guidance as to whether the problem is common to the area or is an isolated case.

When inspecting flats the valuer should be sure to inspect the exterior of the whole block for structural movement, as problems in one part of the block could blight all the flats in it. The particular problems posed by flats are discussed in Chapter 8, but here it must be stressed that if the valuer has any suspicions at all that the block of flats is subject to abnormal structural movement, he should make a recommendation for advance subject to a satisfactory report from a chartered structural engineer.

Tree Root Damage. Roots of rapidly growing trees, especially poplar, ash, elm and willow, extract moisture from the soil. Houses built with shallow foundations on shrinkable clay are particularly vulnerable. Tree roots can extend in all directions from the base of a tree to a distance equal to $1\frac{1}{2}$ times its height, and shrinkage can take place down to a depth of 3 m. The symptoms are as for differential settlement, with the worst point of the damage generally nearest the tree. The offending trees or trees may be in an adjoining garden or planted on the verge of the road, in which case there may be a claim against the owner of the tree or the local authority. On the other hand, a tree within the grounds of the house being surveyed may be causing damage, or may be a potential source of damage to an adjoining house, in which case a claim can be expected. It does not take so many years for a small tree to grow into a large one and the valuer must be on the lookout for recently planted trees which are going to cause trouble as they mature. In cases of severe tree root damage the valuer will have no option but to advise that the property is unsuitable for mortgage. In cases of recently planted trees in potentially hazardous positions, a retention or undertaking can ensure their early removal. Mature trees which are in potentially damaging positions but which have not yet caused damage pose something of a dilemma. A large tree can absorb 54,000 litres (12,000 gallons) of water per year from the ground. When a tree, or several such trees, are removed, the additional moisture in the ground can cause swelling or heave, with parts of the building being forced upwards, showing the reverse effects of settlement and with vertical cracks wider at the top than at the bottom.

Clay Shrinkage. This can cause predominantly diagonal cracks across the corner of a building affecting the two adjacent walls with a stepped form of crack in brickwork or blockwork.

Usually the foundation has not been taken deep enough to avoid the shrinkage of the clay sub-soil which occurs when it becomes dry, as it may do during very hot weather or by extraction of the water by tree roots. Drying out is likely to be greatest at the corner of a building; its effects will generally be observed first at the end of a long dry summer and may occur suddenly. This defect is more common in the south-east of England where there is a combination of shrinkable clay sub-soils and fairly dry weather.

Underground Workings. A valuer whose practice is in an area of coal mining or brine extraction will be aware of the effects of mining subsidence with which localised parts of his area are likely to be affected. He will know the likely response of the Board involved so far as compensation is concerned and the effects of mining subsidence on house prices in his area. A valuer outside his own area is at a disadvantage so far as mining subsidence is concerned, as underground workings can extend several miles from the pithead.

Settlement arising from tunnelling works can present a serious problem, perhaps with a long drawn-out battle to get any redress. With many 19th century urban sewers being replaced at the present time by means of tunnelling, this problem is not all that uncommon.

Bulging of Walls. Once a wall has started to bulge, the tendency is for it to continue to do so, unless restrained, until it reaches a state where rebuilding is essential. Rebuilding of a gable or front wall can be a very expensive operation. Careful visual observation should indicate whether a wall is bulging or not. Further evidence is often provided by opening up of the joints between door and window frames and the wall. Internally there will often be a gap between the bulging wall and the first floor boards or staircase. The cause of bulging walls is normally inadequate thickness in relation to their length and height, coupled with lack of lateral restraint. Sometimes just the outer skin of the wall has bulged, often as a result of corroded wall ties coupled with perished mortar. Horizontal cracks at about 1 m intervals in brickwork are evidence of rusted wall ties. Gable ends of terraced houses are particularly vulnerable to bulging, especially when the staircase runs up the gable. Front walls of terraces with heavy overhanging cornices are also vulnerable. Bulging wall problems can be accentuated by vibrations from a near-by main road or railway or from pile-driving on a near-by construction site. The presence of tie rods, with their associated cast iron or steel plates on the face of the brickwork, is always an immediate indication that there has been trouble in the past. As with differential settlement, the surveyor will be anxious to determine if any of the movement is of recent origin: generally the condition of joints at the sides of window openings will give the best guide.

Sulphate Attack. Horizontal cracking in the horizontal mortar joints of brickwork built with clay bricks and with the mortar itself having become pliable is probably the result of chemical action on the Portland cement or semi-hydraulic lime in the mortar by the soluble sulphate salts commonly present in bricks, producing a considerable increase in the volume of the mortar. The action requires the presence of water and the defect is usually associated with brickwork which remains wet for an appreciable time.

Sulphate attack of the Portland cement in the concrete or in the mortar joints of the brickwork in the foundations causes the concrete and/or the mortar to expand and hence lift the walls. If a solid ground floor of concrete has no damp-proof membrane underneath it there may also be cracking and lifting of the floor. Sulphates in fill-material used under ground floor slabs sometimes cause lateral expansion, pushing walls outward by up to 6 mm to give a characteristic overhang at damp-proof course level.

Unlined chimney stacks serving gas boilers and fires may be subject to sulphate attack, causing them to crack and lean.

Thermal Expansion. This problem usually shows itself in vertical cracks in long lengths of brickwork. Its occurences, so far as domestic property is concerned, are mainly limited to modern brick-built terraces of houses without expansion joints and often built in sand-lime or concrete bricks which have a high co-efficient of thermal expansion. Another area where thermal expansion is found is in long parapet walls.

Moisture Expansion. A predominantly straight vertical crack near the corner of a building, extending upwards from the ground level d.p.c., is likely to be the result of moisture expansion of clay bricks, sometimes in conjunction with thermal movement. The lateral expansion may produce a crack at the point of least restraint, which in the case of straight elevations is often at the corner of the building: it will generally be accompanied by some over-sailing of the brickwork on the damp-proof course.

Spalling Brickwork. This defect occurs in concrete framed buildings with brick cladding panels when the brick cladding is too rigid to tolerate the compressive force progressively applied and the concrete frame shrinks and creeps.

Surface disintegration of bricks may occur due to frost action or to salt action or to both. Under-burnt bricks are particularly vulnerable.

Stonework which is not laid on the natural bed is likely to weather very badly.

Bricks which contain pieces of chalk, limestone or calcite will tend to suffer some surface disintegration or blowing.

Beam and Lintel Defects. Here the evidence is likely to be cracking or disturbance of bricks and plaster at the ends of lintels, coupled with deflection and cracking of the brickwork. The cause may be a lintel or beam of inadequate size. Timber beams are especially prone to deflection. More likely causes are the rotting of timber beams or rusting of steel ones. When timber rots it weakens and tends to be compressed; when steel rusts it expands, with consequent effects on the wall in each case.

Sometimes, particularly in new houses, lintels are missed out altogether with the wall just carried on the window frame! The beams over bay window openings are a regular source of trouble, often because dampness has got in through the bay roof, causing rot in the beam. Whether defective beams and lintels can be replaced easily or not will depend on their position in the building and on the nature of the building itself. In extreme cases the extent of the problem will be such as to make the property unsuitable for mortgage; other cases will be dealt with by means of a retention or, if the surveyor is not sure of the situation, he can ask that the applicant obtains a detailed investigation and estimate.

Rusting or Corrosion of Metalwork. Bulging or cracking caused by the rusting of lintels or beams has already been mentioned.

Horizontal cracks at regular intervals in brickwork are a sign that ferrous metal cavity ties have rusted.

Cracking tends to occur in brickwork and stonework where metal handrails, etc., are built into the wall and rusting has occurred.

The breakdown of the surface of reinforced or *in situ* concrete walls, cladding panels or columns, is not uncommon, with the steel reinforcement rusting and forcing off the surface of the concrete.

Geological Faults. These are not very common, and, so far as the building society surveyor is concerned, local knowledge of how these affect his area is likely to be important.

Seismic Tremors and Earthquakes. This is not generally a problem in the U.K.

When the valuer has completed his inspection and noted the various evidences of structural movement, he is faced with making his recommendation. He may well have a good idea of the cause of the problem he has found and be fairly sure in his own mind as to whether movement is continuing or not. However, he is not called upon to do more than can be done at one fairly brief visit and should be cautious in the extreme about making categorical statements on matters about which he cannot be certain. There are several options open to the valuer in cases of structural movement. Where the effects are severe or there is evidence of significant recent movement, the property is best turned down. Where the effects are less severe and evidence of recent movement is only minimal, it is suggested that any advance should be recommended subject to a satisfactory report from a chartered civil or structural engineer. Where the damage is obviously localised and not likely to have any far-reaching effects (e.g. as in the case of a rotten or missed lintel) a retention or undertaking may be appropriate. In cases of very long-standing movement where the structural stability is in no way impaired and where there is no evidence of any recent movement (say within the last 20 years) it is probable that the building has reached a state of equilibrium or repose and in these circumstances the valuer may feel that the dangers of further movement are so remote that he can safely recommend the house as suitable for an advance without further ado, albeit perhaps not a maximum advance; if this is done the presence of the long-standing settlement should nevertheless be recorded in the Building Society report (if for no other reason than to protect the valuer from any suggestion that he had negligently failed to notice the settlement) even though it will probably mean that the insurance company will restrict subsidence cover and this may cause the building society to offer a less than maximum advance.

3.2. Dampness

Second only to structural movement in the possible extent of its consequences is dampness. Dampness is unhealthy, often causes unsightly markings to walls and ceilings, but more significantly is a pre-requisite for attacks by wet rot, dry rot and Death Watch Beetle.

The main areas and type of dampness which the valuer will encounter are:

Sub-floor dampness. Prior to the 1965 Building Regulations it was common to construct suspended ground floors with a void beneath them, extending down as far as the foundations. It is hardly surprising that this void should sometimes act as a reservoir and collect ground water from the surrounding area. The prevalence of this defect led to the current Building Regulation requirement that the surface of the sub-floor should be above outside ground level; this has had the result of reducing sub-floor voids to a nominal depth and has led to an increasing use of solid ground floors in new houses. Water under the floor is often very difficult to get rid of. Someti.nes a drain can be introduced, but this is hardly ideal, as the sub-floor surface remains wet. Sometimes field drains can be laid around the house, connected into a water course, soak-away, or main drain via a silt pit. But on a low-lying site this is often not possible and the only alternative may be to line the sub-floor space with waterproof rendering (on the assumption that the sub-floor surface is already of concrete) or fill the void with gravel to above water-level and concrete over. Where there is significant sub-floor water, the property is best treated as unsuitable for mortgage advance. If the vendor or purchaser comes up with specific proposals and estimates for eliminating the sub-floor water the matter can be re-considered.

As a sub-floor inspection is beyond the scope of the normal building society valuation, sub-floor water is a defect which is often missed and this is one of the main reasons why no purchaser should ever buy a house without having a structural survey carried out on his behalf. Nevertheless, there are often factors which suggest that there may be sub-floor problems and in these cases a mortgage advance can be recommended subject to a satisfactory report on the condition of the sub-floor. These factors include a waterlogged low-lying site (which may of itself be such as to make an advance inadvisable) or a site sloping steeply down to the house; air bricks at or below path level which may be letting water in; rusty nail heads in the floor boards or a high moisture content in the boards. Springy and deflecting floors are other signs of problems beneath. As in many other matters, local knowledge is often a useful guide, and enquiries of the vendor may disclose a history of problems. The presence of rot in floor boards or skirtings is a definite reason for requiring a sub-floor inspection, as is the absence of

air bricks to give cross-ventilation in properties with suspended ground floors.

The sub-floor void may not be holding water but may have a
very damp surface, either of earth or concrete. Slight dampness
is general in older properties, especially in clay soil areas, but if
it is positively wet some treatment is desirable, even if this is
no more than the laying of a polythene damp-proof membrane
with a gravel layer to hold it in place. Very slight sub-floor
dampness will generally do little harm in cases where there are
damp-proof courses below the seatings for the timber joints and
where there is a good cross-ventilation.

Basement Dampness. Where there is a basement, it is often
found that walls and floor are slightly damp. This is almost
inevitable if the basement is not tanked or lined with waterproof rendering. Provided the dampness is only slight it can
normally be accepted. If, however, there is positive evidence of
water getting in, as opposed to mere dampness, then remedial
action is called for. A common point of water entry is at the old
coal chute. As with sub-floors, basements should be ventilated
to minimise the risk of dry rot attack.

Rising Damp. Where a property has no horizontal damp-
proof course, it is probable that the lower parts of the ground
floor walls will show visible evidence of rising damp. A more
accurate assessment of the situation can be made with a
moisture meter, and this is essential in an older house where
ground floor walls have recently been decorated. Rising damp
causes the plaster to perish and decorations to be disfigured. It
is also responsible for rot in skirting boards, fitted cupboards,
etc., and at joist ends. Treatment is by insertion of a damp-proof
course, either silicone injection, or electro-osmotic or a traditional damp-proof course of plastic, lead-cored bituminous felt,
lead or slate. Silicone is the cheapest, although a small percentage of cases do fail at the first attempt. A problem which often
remains after the damp-proof course has been put in is that joist
ends built into solid external walls (and hence probably rotten
anyway) are more often than not left below the level of the new
damp-proof course. Cases of rising damp are generally best
dealt with by means of a retention and the required work
should extend to examining and treating joist ends as necessary.

Floors Below Ground Level. Dampness often occurs when the
outside ground level is above internal floor level, or when soil
has been banked up against the outside wall. A similar case is
that of the build-up of mortar droppings in the base of a cavity,

raising the level of the foot of the cavity above the damp-proof course. Where suspended timber floors are at a level below external ground, ventilation of the sub-floor void is extremely difficult and a sub-floor inspection should normally be required in these cases.

Damp Floors. Ground floors of solid construction are sometimes damp, particularly in the case of flagstone floors. A retention should be made in respect of damp solid floors until such time as they have been either asphalted or concreted with a damp-proof membrane beneath.

Penetrating Dampness. Properties with solid walls often suffer from penetrating dampness, due to the porous nature of the materials from which the walls are constructed. Penetrating dampness may be localised, often associated with a defective gutter or rainwater stack, in which case treatment will probably be relatively easy. Or it can be general, in which case external rendering or the erection of a blockwork inner skin is called for. If the dampness is very extensive, the applicant should be asked to obtain estimates for the remedial work and the application can be considered in the light of these. Localised dampness often occurs around window openings, either below the cills, due to defective pointing, or at the sides, due to penetration through brick or stone or, in the case of cavity walls, due to a defective vertical damp-proof course; or at the head of the window due to a faulty or omitted cavity tray flashing. Small isolated patches of damp on the inner faces of cavity walls probably indicate bridged cavities due to mortar droppings on cavity ties. In exposed places, foam filled cavities have been known to assist penetration of water across the cavity.

The other main area of water penetration is through the roof. Markings on chimney breasts, on the upper floors, are very common, indicating defective chimney flashings and probably poor pointing to the stack as well. Other damp patches may occur on upper floor ceilings, due to missing slates or tiles, defective flashings, perforated valley or parapet gutter linings, omission of damp-proof courses in parapet walls, or perforations in sheet coverings of lead, copper, zinc, asphalt or felt. Felt roofs are particularly vulnerable, especially as ponding so often occurs on them. The life of most felt roofs is only about 15 years.

Another source of damp markings on ceilings is snow driven through gaps in the tiling where there is no underfelting, as in general in larger old houses.

The extent of dampness getting through the roof covering will determine whether the valuer recommends a retention or undertaking or asks that the applicant obtains a structural report on the condition of the roof and estimates for its repair. This is prudent where there is anything other than trivial dampness as it could be that the damp which is visible has caused other defects which are not visible without an inspection of the roof void itself; also the presence of several slipped slates may be an indication that slate nails are rusted through or that battens are rotten and that the whole of the roof needs re-slating.

Condensation. The other major source of damp problems is condensation. Water vapour is normally present in the air in varying quantities and some will be converted to water when the air comes into contact with relatively cold surfaces. Such condensation may appear on the internal surfaces of a building or as interstitial condensation within the construction, from where it may feed through a crack to appear possibly some distance from its point of origin. Interstitial condensation can go on for a long time, leading to extensive rot before its presence becomes visually obvious. The sources of condensation are construction water—several tonnes of which are used in a single house; occupational water—in addition to water vapour from cooking, washing and bathing, there is vapour from the occupants themselves (one adult producing half a litre of water in 9 hours simply from breathing); paraffin stoves produce 1 litre of water vapour per litre of paraffin burnt; excessive amounts of cleaning water make a contribution, especially when it seeps under floor coverings. The amount of water which condenses in some properties, especially flats, is considerable, leading to a state of almost permanent dampness and providing suitable conditions for mould growth.

Condensation often first becomes apparent in the corners of rooms, especially kitchens, cold bedrooms and built-in cupboards, where there is little heat and not much air movement. Beads of moisture appear on the surface of dense finishes, metal fixings tend to rust and mould growth appears. Condensation will occur first on the coldest surfaces, the cold bridges of window frames and surfaces of concrete lintels, the corners of a building, especially those formed by a concrete flat roof or suspended concrete floor where the edge of the roof or floor extends to the exterior wall. The situation is always worse where ventilation is inadequate. Remedial work may include a combination of improved ventilation, more adequate or better distribution of heat and a high standard of thermal insulation. Better ventilation can be achieved by air vents, either fixed in the walls or windows or above cooking and washing applicances and by keeping the windows slightly open. The provision of background heating in bedrooms should be considered. Thermal insulation can be improved by fixing insulating sheets or boards to the internal faces of the external walls, or by filling the cavities with insulating materials where the property is not subject to severe exposure.

Interstitial condensation occasionally takes place in walls but is more common in roofs/ceilings. In a roof/ceiling construction not having a water vapour barrier at ceiling level or below the insulated roof finish, there will be a dew point gradient through the structure and if the temperature at any position falls below the dew point at that position then condensation will take place. During the winter months there are likely to be a number of occasions when the surface of the roof finish becomes very cold and the risk of condensation is then high. Summer conditions which result in a heavy dew outside are also high risk times. The condensed water accumulated in the roof structure, because it cannot evaporate through the roof finish, eventually leaks though cracks or other channels to the underside of the ceiling, where it causes a damp patch. In a similar manner, residual construction water which has been trapped may show itself as a damp patch under the same conditions as condensation or during cold rainy weather: this is a particular problem with concrete roofs or roofs where wet screeds have been laid.

Remedial work may include the provision of an efficient vapour barrier at ceiling level, ventilation of the air space of flat roofs of hollow construction of the fitting of ventilators on the external surface of the roof. In the case of timber flat roofs, in addition to the provision of a vapour barrier at ceiling level, it is necessary to provide for ventilation of cavities between roof joists. Interstitial condensation in timber flat roofs can lead to serious outbreaks of dry rot, sometimes necessitating complete renewal of a roof.

Where a single damp patch shows on the surface of a chimney breast or flue serving an open fire it may be due to the presence of salts in the plaster, derived from acid flue gas reacting with lime etc. in the bricks and/or mortar. The salts from the flue pass to the surface of the internal plaster work and then absorb moisture from the room, especially when the humidity of the air is high. Damp areas on the plaster work of the chimney serving gas or oil-fired heating appliances are usually caused by condensation of some of the water vapour in the flue gases in cases where the flue is unlined.

Burst Pipes. The remaining source of dampness is that from burst pipes, leaking tanks, dripping overflows, etc. Waste pipes under baths and the base of the vertical soil stack are common places. Leakages in drains in the sub-floor void are not uncommon. More difficult to diagnose are bursts in pipes buried in walls or fractures in heating pipes buried in floors or located in floor ducts.

In virtually every case of dampness in the proximity of timber there is the threat of it leading to a severe outbreak of rot. If this occurs the security provided by the affected property may be impaired. The building society valuer must therefore treat all dampness seriously. Only the most minor cases can be dealt with by means of an undertaking. More severe cases, when the source of the problem and the necessary remedial work are clear, can be dealt with by a retention. Where there is extensive dampness or the source is not clear, the applicant should be asked to arrange for a detailed investigation by an architect or building surveyor and to obtain a builder's estimate for remedial work. When these are to hand the matter can be re-considered. In the worst cases there will be no option but to advise against accepting the property as security for mortgage advance.

3.3. Defects in Timber

Wet Rot. The most common timber defect which the valuer will meet will be wet rot to window frames and cills, door frames and doors, timber gutters and weather-boarding, generally due to the breakdown of the paint film and the saturation of the timber over a period of time. A similar condition is likely to be encountered in joist ends and timber lintels built into damp brickwork without adequate protection.

Depending upon the nature and extent of the wet rot, the valuer will recommend a retention or an undertaking.

Beetle Infestation. To check completely a property for evidence of beetle infestation is a time-consuming exercise, involving inspection of floor and roof voids. This is beyond the scope of a building society survey, but the valuer should nevertheless be on the lookout for any evidence of beetle attack in exposed surfaces of floor boarding or roof beams. If evidence of attack is found, or if external inspection of the roof indicates deflection of roof timbers, then the applicant should be required to obtain a detailed report from a specialist firm or surveyor.

In some cases active infestation will have ceased many years ago and the attack will be of little practical significance. However, the building society valuer is not in a position to make the extensive investigations necessary to confirm that the attack is no longer active and whenever there is any evidence of beetle attack a specialist report should normally be called for.

If left untreated, the infestation can continue until the strength of the floor boards, joists, purlins, rafters, ceiling bearers and other timbers is so seriously weakened that they will have to be replaced, at great expense. For this reason any work recommended as necessary by a specialist report should be made the subject of a retention.

Common Furniture Beetle, Anobium Punctatum. The incidence of this beetle is widespread. It can occur in properties within 10 years of construction, especially if infected articles such as old furniture have been stored in the roof space.

The damage is done by the larvae, which hatch from eggs laid in cracks in the wood, in joints of made-up woodwork and, more rarely in old flight holes. The larvae travel along the grain, but as they feed and grow they tunnel in all directions, filling their galleries with loosely packed granular frass. The adult beetles are between 3 and 10 mm in length. The life cycle from egg to adult beetle is between one and three years. Adult beetles emerge in the summer months and mate, when the females lay their eggs in suitable places. The beetle is found in old furniture, hardwood constructional timbers in period houses and in the sapwood of softwoods in buildings of all ages. Attack in softwood timbers may develop to the extent of causing some timbers to collapse, if sufficient sapwood is present.

Longhorn Beetle, Hylotrupes Bajulus. Active infestation is limited to Surrey and Essex. Only the sapwood of softwoods is attacked. The larvae tunnel just beneath the surface, completely destroying sapwood behind the shell of apparently sound wood. The life cycle is a long one, upwards of ten years, with the result that serious damage may result before the first flight holes bring the attack to light. If the attack is active, drastic remedial measures are called for. If the proportion of sapwood is high, the damage may sometimes be so serious as to call for complete replacement of roof timbers.

Lyctus Beetles. These are mainly pests of seasoning yards but re-infestation may occur if timber containing active infestation

is utilized for such purposes as furniture, panelling and flooring. Attack is confined to the sapwood of certain hardwoods
only. The sapwood of carcassing timber in period houses is
quite likely to have been affected by lyctus attack. In modern
developments lyctus infestation is most likely to be found in
the sapwood of oak flooring and joinery and it is then usual to
recommend the renewal of all timber containing sapwood.

Death Watch Beetle, Xestobium Refuvillosum. This beetle
lays eggs in crevices, cracks or old exit holes and the larvae do
the damage by tunnelling in and feeding on the wood. Attack is
usually confined to old timbers of several species of hardwoods
but it has been known to spread to adjacent softwood timbers
and has occasionally been found in property containing no
hardwoods. Adequate moisture and the presence of fungal
decay are conditions favourable for infestation. The galleries
made by the larvae are about 3 mm in diameter and filled with
coarse frass. The adult beetle is brown or red brown in colour
and varies from 6 to 10 mm in length. There are patches of
short yellow hairs on the wing cases, which give the beetle a
mottled appearance. The length of the life cycle is dependent
upon the moisture content of the timber, the presence and
extent of fungal decay and the temperature. In optimum
conditions the life cycle may be only one year but in less
favourable conditions it may be prolonged to two or several
years. The common area of attack is the end of hardwood
structural timbers and trusses which have become damp where
built into external walls. Unfortunately major structural damage may well have occurred before the attack is discovered.

Ambrosia Beetles. The adult beetles tunnel spirally, at right
angles to the grain, in living and newly felled logs prior to
importation. Whilst the timber may be disfigured there is little
risk of spread of attack or of infection of other timbers and
attack by this type of beetle is of no practical significance.

Woodboring Weevil. Both beetles and larvae bore in timber,
causing damage resembling that of the common furniture
beetle. Both hardwoods and softwood are liable to infestation
but a pre-requisite of attack is generally the presence of decay,
and hence weevil infestation is most likely to be found in
basements and sub-floor spaces where fungal decay has
become established.

Bark Beetle. This beetle is often mistaken for the common
furniture beetle but its activity is confined to the waney edges
of carcassing timbers.

Fungal Attack. Fungal attack of timbers is likely to be much more serious than beetle infestation, because the strength of the attacked timbers is seriously reduced. Eradication involves renewal of affected timbers and often extensive consequential work to, for example, plaster cornices.

In view of this any suspicions of fungal attack should put the building society valuer on his guard and he should require the applicants to obtain a specialist report or structural survey of the property. The ideal habitat for fungal growth is damp, inadequately ventilated and preferably warm. Common areas of attack are damp and inadequately ventilated basements and sub-floor spaces, the backs of skirtings, window frames and panelling where these butt against damp walls, and timbers beneath leaking parapet gutters. The main timber attacking fungae are referred to below.

True Dry Rot—Merulius Lacrymans. This is by far the most important and devastating of the wood rotting fungae. It produces a cubicle breakdown of timber and total loss of strength.

Initial evidence of attack may be no more than slight waviness on the surface of panelling, skirtings and linings which when removed may reveal extensive infestation. Infected unventilated rooms usually have a typical musty smell. In damp conditions in still air the fungus develops a white fluffy mass, spreading over the surface of the wood. In drier conditions it forms a grey-white felt over the wood, sometimes with patches of yellow or lilac. Branching strands of hyphae then develop, travelling rapidly and able to penetrate brickwork to get to other timber. In suitable conditions fruiting bodies will occur, usually fleshy plates of fungus with white margins and the centre covered with rust red spores, sometimes produced in such quantities that a room may become covered with an ejected layer of these red spores. As these fruiting bodies grow out into the air and light, they are sometimes the first indication of dry rot in a building.

Phellinus. This fungus is similar to merulius and requires similar treatment.

Cellar Fungus, Coniophora Cerebella. This is very similar to merulius except that in the final stages the wood often develops longitudinal splits or cracks. The hyphae are normally brown or black and spread over the face of a wall in a fern-like pattern. Fruiting bodies are rare.

The treatment of fungal attack normally involves the removal of all affected timbers and their replacement with fresh impregnated timber, removal of plasterwork, etc., to a distance 1 m beyond the ends of the hyphae strands and the impregnation of all surfaces in the area with fungicidal fluid. Equally important is to eradicate the damp condition which was probably responsible for the outbreak.

3.4. Check List of Common Defects

The most serious defects which the building society valuer is likely to encounter are structural movement of foundations and walls, dampness and timber defects. These are discussed above in sections **3.1.**, **3.2.** and **3.3.** respectively.

The number and variety of possible defects is enormous and the list below is in no way exhaustive. For illustrations of most common defects together with notes on causes and remedial work the reader is referred to "Common Defects in Buildings" by H. J. Elldridge.

Walls:
Structural Problems

Inadequate foundations
Differential settlement
Shrinkage or swelling of clay sub-soil
Tree root damage
Made up ground
Underground operations
Missed lintels
Rusting or rotten lintels
Thermal movement
Moisture expansion of brickwork/blockwork
Shrinkage of blockwork
Shrinkage of in situ concrete
Cracking and spalling of concrete walls, panels or columns
Bulging of walls
Omission of cavity wall ties
Corrosion of cavity wall ties
Spread of structural roof
Sulphate attack on cement mortar
Frost damage causing movement of brickwork at d.p.c.

Damp problems

Damp basement walls
Bridged damp-proof course
Omission of damp-proof course

Bridged cavity
Penetrating dampness—solid walls (especially if only 100 mm)
Split or punctured cavity gutters
Condensation on internal surfaces
Interstitial condensation
Effects of leaking overflows or gutters
Damp patches on chimney breasts
Defective vertical damp-proof courses

Defects affecting wall finishes

Spalling brickwork (in panels of concrete framed building)
Surface disintegration of brickwork due to frost or salt action
Lime blows in brickwork
Soft mortar
Re-pointing needed
Stonework wrongly bedded
Surface deterioration of stonework
Rusting of metalwork built into walls
Cracking of rendering
Rendering broken away due to underburnt bricks
Hollow rendering
Flaking rendering
Blistering of paint on rendering
Loose applied tile finishes
Damaged slate hanging
Damaged tile hanging
Rotten weatherboarding
Cracked asbestos panels

Floors:
Suspended floors

Collapse due to fungal or insect attack
Excessive deflection
Joists not wedged on to sleeper walls
Inadequate sub-floor ventilation
Sub-floor water
Sinking of surface of sub-floor causing sleeper walls to settle
Excessive dampness in timbers
Boards curling
Excessive gaps between boards
Loose boards

Rotten boards
No sub-floor access

Solid floors

No damp-proof membrane
Damp-proof membrane by-passed at edges
Condensation at edges of solid floors
Settlement of concrete floor
Sulphate attack on concrete floor
Screeds cracking or breaking up
Screeds lifting or hollow

Roofs:
Pitched roofs

Spread of structural roof
Structural elements not tied together
Rot or beetle
Sagging of timbers
No insulation
Torching falling away
Underfelt torn
Slates slipping
Slates laminating
Nails perished
Tiles laminating
Tiles slipping
Broken tile nibs
Rotten pegs (stone slates)
Slipped hip tiles
Pointing needed to ridge or hips
Cracked tiles
Perforated lead valleys
Battens rotten
Barge boards rotten
Eaves boarding rotten
Skylights rotten

Parapet walls and gutters

Absence of damp-proof course
Defective joint or flashing at junction of roof finish and wall
Defective parapet gutter lining
Blocked gutter outlet

Insufficiently deep parapet gutter
Pointing needed to parapet brickwork
Frost, sulphate or thermal movement of parapet brickwork

Flat roofs

Condensation on underside of flat roofs (interstitial condensation)
Sagging due to rot in timbers
Sagging due to inadequate size of timbers
Ponding due to sagging or inadequate falls
Ponding due to blocked drain outlet
Blistering of asphalt
Splitting of asphalt
Blistering, rippling or cockling of felt
Splitting of felt
No ventilation to timber roof
Perforation of roof covering allowing water entry
Rot or beetle attack in timbers
Expansion of concrete flat roof causing cracking of brickwork
Dampness from residual construction water

Other roof coverings

Cracked asbestos sheets
Rusting galvanised sheets
Perforated leadwork
Leadwork with damaged rolls and drips
Perforated copper or zinc sheeting
Defective thatch

Chimneys

In need of pointing
Stacks leaning
Stacks cracking or splitting
Loose pots
Flashings loose or missing
Dampness on breasts

Rainwater goods

Rotten timber gutters
Corroded metal gutters
Warped plastic gutters
Split or corroded metal downpipes
Bowing plastic downpipes

Blocked rainwater pipes
Defective lead lining to gutters
Inadequate falls to gutters
Gutters needing cleaning out.

Windows

Rotten timber frames
Defective putty or paintwork
Broken or cracked glass
Loose or twisted casements
Casements or sashes needing easing
Missing weights to sliding sashes
Broken/missing ironmongery
Inadequate natural ventilation
Defective mastic pointing externally
Dampness penetrating jambs
Dampness penetrating cill
Rusting metal frames
Bulging leadlights
Excessive condensation
Blocked condensation gutters
Failed double glazed sealed units

Doors

Rot in timber doors and frames
Twisted and distorted doors
Ironmongery needing repair/replacement
Doors requiring easing
Doors binding on floor
Door frames out of square
Dangerous glazing
Doors badly fitting
Doors draughty
Water getting under doors
Mastic pointing needed around frames

Stairs

Broken/worn treads
Unduly steep stairs
No handrails
Loose handrails/balustrades
Excessive deflection—open tread stairs
Dangerously wide gaps between balustrade rails

Wall finishes

> Cracked or crazed plaster
> Loose or hollow-sounding plaster
> Plaster finish coat shelling
> Blowing or pitting of plaster
> Perished plaster
> Loose tiling
> Crazed tiling
> Rot or beetle in timber panelling
> Blistered paintwork
> Loose wallpaper

Floor finishes

> Woodblocks lifting or arching
> Clay tiles lifting or arching
> PVC tiles lifting
> PVC sheet curling at edges
> Brick or stone paving cracked or worn
> Floor tiles cracked or worn
> Other finishes badly worn

Ceiling finishes

> Condensation—cold bridge below projecting balcony
> Lath and plaster ceilings collapsed, bulging or cracking
> Plasterboard ceilings—cracks between boards at edges
> Loss of plaster adhesion
> Damaged/loose polystyrene tiles
> Paint flaking
> Loose wallpaper
> Damp markings

Services:

Water

> Inadequate pressure
> Leaking pipes/joints
> Defective ball valves/leaking overflows
> Leaks in galvanised tanks
> Furring of hot water pipes
> Dripping taps

Electricity

> **Obsolete** socket outlets, switches etc.

Failure of insulation
Loose cables
Re-wiring needed
Defective/broken switches, socket outlets

Gas

Corroded pipes
Leaks

Heating

Damaged fire backs
Perforated back boiler
Old-fashioned/defective gas fires
Ditto electric fires
Damaged solid fuel stoves
Old-fashioned central heating system
Furring of central heating pipework
Loose radiators
Inadequate system
Leaks at joints
Leaks in oil supply tank or pipe
Inadequate ventilation for boiler
Fire risks
Clocks/thermostats defective

Drainage

Blocked gulleys
Loose gulleys
Pointing needed behind gulleys
Grids missing
Drains blocked
Drains broken
Brickwork to manholes needing pointing
Manhole covers loose/broken
Soil vent pipes cracked/broken joints
Waste pipes leaking
Waste pipes sagging
Defective septic tank
Defective sewage pump

Fixtures and Fittings:
Kitchen fittings

Cracked ceramic sink

Chipped enamel sink
Loose sink top
Gap behind sink
Damaged sink unit
Damaged taps
Waste disposal unit not working
Damaged/loose worktops
Damaged/loose cupboards
Broken cupboard doors
Loose cooker point
Broken extract fan

Sanitary fittings

Cracked W.C. pedestal
Obsolete W.C.
Leak to w.c. waste pipe
Ball valve needing adjustment
Marked cast iron bath
Split plastic bath
Gap at edges of bath
Obsolete/defective taps
Defective shower fitting
Cracked washbasin
Loose washbasin
Loose bidet
Loose tiles to shower compartment
Loose plastic panels to shower compartment

Heating fixtures

Damaged fireplace surrounds and hearths

Other fixtures

Loose or ill-fitting doors to airing cupboards
Ditto to built-in wardrobes
Mould growth inside cupboards/wardrobes
Loose shelves
Damaged built-in furniture

Outbuildings

Check list generally as above

Paths and grounds

Uneven flagging
Tarmac/concrete breaking up
Potholes
Risk of flooding
Trees too near buildings
Uncultivated gardens
Waterlogged ground

Boundary walls and fences

No gates
Rotten/broken gates
Damaged gate piers
Loose copings to gate piers
Bulging retaining walls
Cracked brick walls
Brick walls needing pointing
Disintegrating bricks
Loose copings
Walls needing rebuilding
Rotten fences
No fences
Hedges needing cutting

3.5. Estimating Costs of Repairs

In order to determine an appropriate level of retentions the valuer will have to estimate the costs of carrying out the necessary repair work which is to be the subject of the retention.

To do this from first principles it is necessary to work out a basic unit price for each item of work involved and multiply this by the appropriate number of units of work. The unit price is built up from five elements.

(1) The labour constant, *i.e.*, the number of man hours needed to do the unit of work.

(2) The labour rate. This varies between London/Liverpool and other places. There are different rates for craftsmen and labourers. The costs of employing a craftsman (Grade A rate—outside London) as at October, 1978, is set out below. In addition to the basic rate an incentive is added to attract labour

and this must be adjusted, based on local knowledge. The labour rate should normally include

> basic wage for 40 hour week,
> 25% incentive bonus, including guaranteed minimum bonus,
> joint board supplement,
> some overtime allowance,
> tool money,
> sick pay premium,
> public holidays,
> National Insurance Contribution,
> annual holiday credit and death benefit,
> Construction Industry Training Board levy and training,
> redundancy reserve, and
> inclement weather guarantee

but it will not include travel-time or allowances, supervision, insurances, profit and overheads.

(3) Costs of materials. These will normally be obtained from a current price list.

(4) Overheads and profit. This figure varies enormously, generally increasing for small works. Additions of 10% on material costs and 100% on labour costs are not uncommon.

(5) Use or hire of scaffolding, plant and vehicles.

A problem exists so far as the rates are concerned in that information in the better known price-books is often irrelevant so far as repairs are concerned, for the following reasons.

(a) They are mainly appropriate to larger new contracts and even in the sections headed "Alterations and Additions" they do not deal with minor repair works, e.g. to quote from Spon's "Architects and Builders Price Book," 1978 Edition, "Jobbing work is outside the scope of this example and no attempt has been made to include prices for such work".

(b) The rates are frequently out of date, e.g. Spon's 1979 Edition is based on market prices of materials current in March/April 1978.

Whilst there are publications which do give labour constants and rates for minor works and repairs, such as Crystal-Smith's "Estimating for Repairs and Small New Works", the problem remains that any published figures, other than labour constants, are soon out of date in times of inflation. For this reason, in order to keep up-to-date with prices, it is necessary to have a constantly up-dated source of information. One source of such up-to-date information on prices for small works is the monthly Estimating Supplement to the Building Trades Journal.

However, as with all valuations, local knowledge of rates being charged in the area will always be better than reference to nationally published figures.

Example (as at October 1978)

Calculate the retention to be held in connection with a mortgage on a detached house with pitched roof and gables, to cover the costs of replacing corroded cast-iron gutters and rainwater pipes. It is assumed these will be replaced in plastic. The house is 10 m long and 6 m to eaves. There is one rainwater pipe at the front and one at the rear.

Extract from rates given in Building Trades Journal "Rehabilitation of older houses" as at October, 1978, including a margin for overheads and profits at 20%.

Description of Work	Unit	Labour Constant (Man hours)	Labour	Material	Unit Price
Taking down and removing existing gutters or pipes up to two storeys high	Lin.M.	0·40	0·77	—	0·92
100 mm plastic half round gutter and brackets	Lin.M.	0·50	0·96	1·37	2·80
Extra for angles	No.	0·40	0·77	2·00	3·32
Extra for outlets	No.	0·40	0·77	1·63	2·98
63 mm plastic rainwater pipe	Lin.M.	0·50	0·96	0·92	2·24
Extra for shoe	No.	0·33	0·63	0·46	1·31

From local knowledge of several recent similar jobs with different contractors it is known that prices being charged and paid in the area for this type of small repair work are being calculated on the basis of a 10% addition to material costs for overheads and profits plus a 50% addition to labour costs for overheads and profit. The published rates, as above, are therefore adjusted to take into account local conditions as set out below.

Work	Unit	Quantity	Material	Labour
Taking down and removing existing gutters or pipes up to two storeys high	Lin.M.	32	—	24.64
100 mm plastic half round gutter and brackets	Lin.M.	20	27·40	19·20
Extra for outlets	No.	2	3·26	1·54
63 mm plastic rainwater pipe	Lin.M.	12	11·04	11·52
Extra for shoe	No.	2	0·92	1·26
			42·62	58·16
Add 10% and 50% respectively			4·26	29·08
			46·88	87·24
Add for travelling expenses				46·88
and use of lorry say				10·00
			Total	144·12
Add for V.A.T. at 8%				11·53
Suggested retention say £160				155·65

(N.B. V.A.T. increased to 15% from June 1979)

In many areas jobbing work of this type will cost more than published rates from sources such as the above and the appropriate additional percentage will have to be added based on local experience.

Laxton's "Building Price Book", 1979, which has a substantial section devoted to Small Works and Alterations, indicates that the prices given are for contracts in the range £25,000–£50,000 but suggests that the following percentages may be added to rates for contracts of smaller value.

Not exceeding £5,000 ....add 35% to 50%
£50,000 to £15,000 ....add 20 %
£15,000 to £25,000 ....add 10%

For certain types of work of a specialist nature, it will be necessary to have the benefit of rates or estimates from a suitable specialist contractor in order to determine the costs of the necessary work.

The building society fee scale does not cover for working out the costs of repairs from first principles in each case and in practice the valuer will often use "spot" figures, based on his previous experience.

Chapter 4

Acts and Regulations

4.1. Unfit Houses and Clearance Areas

Local authorities have a duty to inspect their districts and keep records of the unfit houses. They have powers to require owners to repair unfit houses which can be made fit at reasonable cost. Where this is not the case they have power to secure the closing or demolition of unfit houses.

Whilst, since 1968, an owner-occupier can receive compensation up to full compulsory purchase value as if the house were not unfit, *i.e.* basically market value, this concession may not extend to a mortgagee in possession, who may receive nominal site value only.

Section 15 of the Compulsory Purchase Act 1965 deals with the situation where the compulsory purchase money is insufficient to pay off the mortgage. In the absence of agreement between the mortgagee, the mortgagor and the authority, the compensation payable in respect of the mortgagee's interest and in respect of the equity of redemption will be determined by the Lands Tribunal. See, for example, *Wilson v London County Council* (1954), 5P & CR122. There are also provisions whereby the authority may execute a deed poll vesting the mortgagee's interest in themselves should he fail to convey or make good a title.

Thus it will be appreciated that any property which is likely to be declared unfit during the term of a mortgage is of dubious security and the valuer will not want to recommend it for mortgage.

A check with the public health department of the local authority will indicate if the property concerned is on a current list of unfit houses. If it is not, a useful guide to the local authority's attitude to the property, or at least to properties in the near-by area, can often be obtained by ascertaining whether improvement grants are being made in the area, or only intermediate grants, or no grants at all. Normally a local authority may only approve an application for an intermediate grant if they are satisfied that the property will remain fit for human habitation for at least 15 years, or in certain circumstances at least 10 years. Before making an improvement grant on a property the local authority must be satisfied that the dwelling will provide satisfactory housing accommodation for such period as may be prescribed by the Secretary of State, which circular 64/69 gives as 30 years or such shorter period as the local authority may determine (being not less than 10 years). It is the normal policy of most authorities to adhere to the 15 and 30 year periods: this policy can be checked with the authority and if found to be the case a short-term mortgage could be considered on properties where intermediate grants are being made, and a mortgage over the normal maximum term for the age and type of property where improvement grants are being given.

In addition the valuer will be able to take into account the condition of the property, with particular reference to "unfitness for human habitation" which in the Housing Act 1957 as amended by the Housing Act 1969 is referred to as follows: "In determining for any of the purposes of this Act, whether a house is unfit for human habitation, regard shall be had to its condition in respect of the following matters, that is to say

(a) Repairs
(b) Stability
(c) Freedom from damp
(d) Internal arrangement
(e) Natural lighting
(f) Ventilation
(g) Water supply
(h) Drainage and sanitary conveniences
(j) Facilities for preparation and cooking of food and for disposal of waste water,

and the house shall be deemed to be unfit as aforesaid if and only if, it is so far defective in one or more of the said matters that it is not reasonably suitable for occupation in that condition".

In addition, by section 5 of the 1957 Act, any back-to-back house is regarded as unfit for human habitation.

Where there are two or more unfit houses which are, by reason of their bad arrangement, or the narrowness or bad arrangement of the streets, dangerous or injurious to the health of the inhabitants of the area, the local authority may declare an area to be a clearance area. The area may also contain "other buildings" which are not dangerous or injurious to health. It is also part of the requirement of a clearance area that the local authority must be satisfied that the most satisfactory method of dealing with the conditions in the area is the demolition of all the buildings therein.

Thus the valuer must take into account not only the individual house he is inspecting, but the general arrangement of the houses in the vicinity.

Having decided that a house is unfit for human habitation the local authority may require the person having control of it to execute works which the authority will specify in order, in their opinion, to render the house fit for habitation. If this notice is not complied with, the local authority may themselves enter and do the works and recover the costs.

Where the authority are not satisfied that the house can be repaired at reasonable expense, they must proceed by making a demolition order or a closing order or by purchasing the house.

Before making a demolition order or closing order the authority must give the person having control of the house, any other person who is an owner thereof and every mortgagee the opportunity to make an offer to carry out such works as in their opinion will make the house fit or give an undertaking not to use the premises for human habitation, and the authority may if they think fit accept such offers or undertakings.

If the owner makes no such offer or undertaking or fails to carry out the works or breaks the undertaking the authority must proceed forthwith to make a demolition order or a closing order.

A closing order is made if

(a) the local authority consider it inexpedient to demolish the house because of the probable effect of demolition upon any other house or buildings,
(b) the house is protected by a Building Preservation Order under the Town and Country Planning Acts or is protected as a building of architectural or historic interest,
(c) the intention is to close part only of the house or building, for example an underground room.

Where a valuer sees houses boarded or bricked up he should immediately be on his guard.

In all other cases a demolition order must be made unless the authority decide to purchase the house. A demolition order becomes operative 21 days after the date of service and must require that the house shall be vacated within a specific time, not being less than 28 days from the date on which the order becomes operative, and that the house shall be demolished within 6 weeks after the expiration of that period or from the date when the house is vacated.

Another power which the authority have is that of acquiring a house instead of making a demolition order, which they can do if satisfied that the house is or can be rendered capable of providing accommodation of a standard which is adequate for the time being.

Where there are several unfit houses together and the authority are of the opinion that the most satisfactory way of dealing with the conditions in the area is the demolition of all the buildings in the area, then the authority is required to declare the area to be a clearance area, subject to suitable alternative accommodation for the persons displaced being available and the authority having sufficient resources.

The authority may proceed by making a clearance order which will secure the demolition of all the buildings in the area but not involving the acquisition of any part of the area by the authority, or by purchasing the land comprised in the clearance area themselves and then carrying out the demolition of the buildings in the area. When a clearance order has become operative the owners of any buildings to which it applies must demolish the buildings before the expiration of 6 weeks from the date on which the buildings are vacated. If any building is not demolished in accordance with the order the local authority must enter and demolish the building and sell the materials.

Unfit houses may also be dealt with under planning powers in certain circumstances and the procedure, powers and duties of local authorities for dealing with unfit houses under planning powers correspond closely with those under the Housing Acts referred to above.

Where a local authority list contains several unfit houses in a particular area, or where there is evidence of closing orders or demolition orders having been made, a valuer acting for a potential mortgagee must proceed with considerable caution. The notorious so-called "red-lining" of certain inner city areas where building society mortgages are not normally granted is in reality no more than the effects of the building society valuer taking note of the existing and likely policies of the local authority, especially in respect of improvement grants.

4.2. Grants, Improvement Areas and Housing Action Areas

Grants

By virtue of the Housing Acts local authorities are obliged to make "intermediate grants" (replacing the old standard grants) where statutory conditions are satisfied. At their discretion they may make Improvement Grants for improving existing houses or converting properties into self-contained flats, Special Grants for the installation of standard amenities in houses in multiple occupation, or Repairs Grants to house owners of limited means in General Improvement and Housing Action Areas.

To be eligible for a grant the following general conditions must be met:

(a) Where a house is for owner-occupation the existing rateable value must not exceed the following limits:-

Conversions in Greater London	£600
Improvements in Greater London	£400
Conversions elsewhere	£350
Improvements elsewhere	£225
Scotland—limits vary by district	

(b) The house was erected prior to 31st December, 1925, with the exception of houses which are to be converted to provide additional housing accommodation.

(c) The applicant must sign a certificate stating that he intends to reside in the improved dwelling as an owner-occupier or that he intends to let the dwelling. Intending owner-occupiers must certify that on or before the first anniversary of the date on which the Authority certifies that the dwelling is fit for occupation, after completion of the relevant works to its satisfaction, and throughout the next four years, the dwelling will be their only or main residence for exclusive occupation for themselves and any members of their household. Landlords must certify that they intend throughout the five years beginning with the certified date to let the property or keep it available for letting to a person other than a member of their family.

If these conditions are subsequently broken the local authority may claim back all the grant plus interest. The D.O.E. has stated that owner-occupiers need not repay the grant where they need to sell the house, where making a profit on the improvement is not the reason for the sale. In practice this release from grant conditions is at the Local Authority's discretion.

Intermediate Grants

These replace the former standard grants and cover the provision of standard amenities together with some repairs and replacements. The amenities, with the maximum eligible amount for each, are as follows:

Fixed bath or shower normally in a bathroom	£180
Wash hand basin	70
Sink	180
Hot and cold water supply at fixed bath or shower	230
Wash hand basin	120
Sink	150
Water closet	270
	1200

In addition a maximum eligible amount of £1500 is available for repairs and replacements.

The grant will be based on the appropriate percentage of the total eligible expense, *i.e.*, 50% normally, 60% in General Improvement Areas or 75% in Housing Action Areas.

Before making an intermediate grant the Council have to be satisfied that on completion of the work the following conditions will be met:

(a) That the standard amenities will be provided for the exclusive use of the occupants.

(b) That the dwelling will be in a good state of repair (disregarding internal decoration) having regard to its age, character and location.

(c) That it will comply with Part F of the Building Regulations as regards roof insulation.

(d) That it will in all other respects be fit for human habitation.

(e) That it is likely to be available for use as a dwelling for at least 15 years.

If all the above requirements cannot reasonably be met, the Council have the discretion to reduce them in certain circumstances.

Improvement Grants

These are grants paid at the discretion of the Council for the improvement of older houses to a high standard, or to provide additional self-contained housing accommodation by converting larger-type houses. Improvement grants can also be given towards the conversion of a barn, shippon, stable or other building into a house, but normally only if the resultant dwelling is for letting purposes.

The amount of grant will be fixed by the Local Authority, not exceeding 50% in normal cases, 60% in General Improvement Areas and 75% in Housing Action Areas.

The upper limit of eligible expense is normally £5,000 per dwelling or £5,800 for each flat where flats are provided by the conversion of a house or other building of three or more storeys (including any basement) but there are higher limits for listed buildings. Not more than 50% of the estimated expense can be allowed for works of repair and replacement in connection with an improvement grant.

There are a wide range of improvements which may, at the discretion of the Local Authority, attract grants, including the following:

Eradication of rising dampness
Plastering of walls not previously plastered
Replacing damp solid floors with impervious floors, e.g., asphalt
Enlargement of windows to create adequate natural lighting and ventilation
Replacing obsolete fireplaces by approved appliances capable of burning smokeless fuel
Replacing a steep or winding staircase with new staircase to comply with the Building Regulations
Provision of a separate service water pipe
Enlarging a sub-standard kitchen by removing an internal wall or chimney breast
Replacing work sink units and working surfaces and providing extra storage units and working surfaces
Renewing unsafe or inadequate electric wiring and power points
Comprehensive roof-work, including stripping and re-slating
Repairs to walls, roof and chimney stacks, by rebuilding or repairing or renewing as the case may be

Provision of adequate yard paving or path paving with concrete flags

Demolition of dilapidated structures in rear yards and repair or replacement of yard walls and gates

In appropriate cases the provision of adequate fire precautions, including fire doors

Central heating forming part of a fully comprehensive improvement scheme but to the ground floor only and provided the cost does not exceed the cost of the other improvement items

Kitchen extensions to replace existing lean-to structures of short-lived materials or where it is not possible to put a kitchen within the main house structure

Re-wiring if part of an overall improvement scheme.

Before making an improvement grant the Local Authority must be satisfied that on completion of the work the house will comply with the following ten-point standard:

(1) Be substantially free from damp
(2) Have adequate natural lighting and ventilation in each habitable room
(3) Have adequate and safe provision throughout for artificial lighting and have sufficient electrical socket outlets for the safe and proper functioning of domestic appliances
(4) Be provided with adequate drainage facilities
(5) Be in a stable structural condition
(6) Have satisfactory internal arrangements
(7) Have satisfactory facilities for preparing and cooking food
(8) Be provided with adequate facilities for heating
(9) Have proper provision for the storage of fuel (where necessary) and for the storage of refuse and
(10) Conform with the specifications applicable to the thermal insulation of roof spaces laid down in Part F of the Building Regulations in force at the date of the grant approval.

And in addition it will on completion have all the standard amenities comprising fixed bath or shower, wash hand basin, sink, all with hot and cold water supply, and internal water closet for the exclusive use of the occupants, will be in a first-class state of repair and will be likely to have a useful life of at least 30 years.

Special Grants

A special grant may be made at the discretion of the Local Authority towards the cost of providing standard amenities which will be shared in houses in multiple occupation where there is no immediate prospect of conversion into permanent separate dwellings.

Repair Grants

These grants are made at the discretion of the Local Authority, for repairs only and not associated with the improvement or conversion of dwellings. They are only available to house-owners with limited means in General Improvement Areas and Housing Action Areas.

Other Grants

Improvement grants can be given for works required for the welfare, accommodation or employment of disabled persons where the existing building is inadequate or unsuitable for those purposes.

Insulation grants are available for 66% up to a maximum of £50 for lagging tanks and pipes in roof spaces and for loft insulation where there is no existing insulation.

Grants for historic buildings in Outstanding Conservation Areas are available through the Historic Buildings Council.

General Improvement Areas

A General Improvement Area is a predominantly residential area which has been defined by the Local Authority as being one in which the amenities ought to be improved by comprehensive action under the Authority's powers under the Housing Acts. It must not include any part of an area already declared to be, or in effect treated as, a clearance area, unless the land has been cleared of buildings. The Local Authority must give wide publicity to the declaration of a General Improvement Area and prepare a plan detailing what it hopes will be carried out.

In such area the intention is that:

(a) all the houses should be brought up to a good standard of amenity and repair by owners with the aid of grants,
(b) the environment in the area should be upgraded by re-surfacing the streets, improving traffic flow, parking facilities and street lighting; tree planting and provision

of pedestrian areas and generally making the area a more pleasant place to live in.

Housing Action Areas

These are areas of housing stress caused by the combination of adverse social conditions such as high occupation density, concentration of multiple occupation, unattractive surroundings and where a high proportion of the houses lack standard amenities and are in poor repair. By declaring a Housing Action Area, the Local Authority are calling for concentrated activity, by way of individual house improvement, rehabilitation and repair, to improve within five years the living conditions of the residents. Environmental works, in the first instance, will be of a limited nature.

For the building society valuer grants and general improvement areas are important in two respects:

(1) Where a Local Authority has made only an intermediate grant (formerly a standard grant) on a property there is a fair indication that the anticipated life of the property is limited and for this reason it will probably not be suitable for mortgage advance, other than perhaps a limited advance over a short term.

Where a discretionary improvement grant has been made it can generally (although there are occasional exceptions) be assumed that the property will have an anticipated life of at least 30 years from the time the work was done and consequently it may well be suitable for mortgage advance.

Where a property is situated in a General Improvement Area, it is reasonable to assume that it has a good life ahead of it. Values in General Improvement Areas tend to rise once the initial improvement work is done and most properties in such areas will be suitable for mortgage advance.

Properties in Housing Action Areas must be considered on their merits but in some cases they will not provide suitable security for mortgage advance, because of the nature of the area in which they are situated and bearing in mind that the declaration of a Housing Action Area is acknowledged to be no more than a holding operation.

(2) Where a property has received or is likely to receive a Local Authority grant, the valuer should draw this to the attention of the building society, stating the amount of the grant if known. In grant-aided cases the advance offered will normally be the recommended percentage of the figure left

when the amount of the grant is deducted from the valuation of the property after completion of the improvement work. The recommended percentage of the value of the property in its unimproved condition may be released on purchase and the balance of the advance on completion of the work, although some societies, having reservations because of the possible subsequent difficulties of ensuring that the borrower does in fact carry out the repairs and improvements, prefer an initial restriction to act as an incentive.

The reason for deducting the amount of the grant from the value on completion is the requirement that the grant should be repaid to the Local Authority if the house is sold within five years of the grant being made. This requirement becomes a charge on the property and as a result the marketability of the property is restricted until the improvement grant is repaid or until the Local Authority formally waive their right to repayment. It is for this reason that it is not uncommon for the building society to require a covenant by the mortgagor against applying, without the consent of the society, for an improvement grant in respect of mortgaged property.

4.3. Planning Permission

If a property does not have the appropriate planning permission there is always a risk that a Planning Authority may serve an enforcement notice requiring the property to be demolished or returned to its former state or use. In this event the property would hardly be good security for mortgage advance and therefore the valuer needs to satisfy himself that planning approvals are in order.

Planning permission is needed for any "development", which is defined in section 290(1) of the Town and Country Planning Act 1971 as:

a) The carrying-out of building operations, engineering operations, mining operations or other operations in, on, over or under land, or

b) The making of any material change in the use of any buildings or other land.

It is also provided, *inter alia*, that the use of a single dwelling for the purpose of two or more separate dwellings constitutes development.

The expression "building operations" includes, besides new buildings,

rebuilding operations

structural alterations of buildings
structural additions to buildings
other operations normally undertaken by a person carrying on business as a builder.

"Building" includes any structure or erection, or any part of a building, as so defined, but does not include plant or machinery comprised in a building.

"Other operations normally undertaken by a builder" includes ancillary demolitions in connection with rebuilding and in connection with alterations. Demolition of part of a building may amount to development.

"Engineering operations" includes the formation or laying out of means of access to highways and "means of access" includes any means of access, whether private or public, for vehicles or pedestrians, and includes the street.

The 1971 Act provides that the following, *inter alia*, shall not constitute development:

(1) Internal or external improvements, alterations, or maintenance works (not constituting the making good of war-damage) none of which materially affects the external appearance of the building so treated, provided that any works begun after December 5th, 1968, for the alteration of a building by providing additional space in the building below ground level will constitue development.

(2) The use of any buildings or other land within the curtilage of a dwelling house for any purpose incidental to the enjoyment of the dwelling house as a dwelling house. "Use" does not involve building operations, so that this section does not authorise erections such as garden sheds but these are permitted, within limitations, by the General Development Order 1973. The lawyers have made a feast out of the definition of "curtilage", which may be defined as "a garden yard, field or piece of void ground lying near and belonging to the dwelling". A line of cases has decided that the curtilage may include a shrubbery and orchards, a paddock behind the house accessible only from the garden, or a courtyard to a house: but that it does not include fields for grazing, gardens and stables on the opposite side of the road purchased subsequently to the house or a private road leading to a mansion.

Where there is doubt as to whether a particular operation or change of use constitutes "development" within the meaning of the 1971 Act, the Act makes provision for the determination of such cases by application to the Local Planning Authority.

The Town and Country Planning General Development Order 1973 gives an automatic planning permission, without any application, for various classes of development known as "permitted development". Those classes relevant to the building society valuer are:

Class 1

(a) The enlargement, improvement or other alteration of a dwelling house so long as

—the cubic content of the original dwelling house (as ascertained by external measurement) is not exceeded by more than 50 m³ or one tenth, whichever is the greater, subject to a maximum of 115 m³,

—the height of the building as so enlarged, altered or improved does not exceed the height of the highest part of the roof of the original dwelling house,

—no part of the building as so enlarged, altered or improved projects beyond the forwardmost part of any wall in the original dwelling house which fronts on a highway, provided that the erection of a garage, stable, loose box or coach house .... within the curtilage of the dwelling house shall be treated as the enlargement of the dwelling house for all purposes of this permission, including the calculation of cubic content

(b) Provision of a porch subject to the area being not more than 2 m², the height not more than 3 m and the porch at least 2 m from the edge of the property fronting a highway.

(c) Provision of or works to any other buildings or enclosures within the curtilage of the dwelling (e.g. summer houses, greenhouses, tool sheds, bee hives, dog kennels, dovecotes, poultry houses, etc.) subject to the height not exceeding 4 m for a ridged roof and otherwise 3 m, not more than 50% of the site (net of dwelling) being covered and no part of the buildings extending forward of the forwardmost part of the existing buildings fronting a highway.

(d) Provision of a hardstanding for vehicles.

(e) Provision of an oil storage tank up to 3,500 litres, not more than 3 m high and not in front of any wall of the house fronting a highway.

Class 2

Provision of, alteration to or improvement of walls, fences and gates not exceeding 1 m in height when abutting on a road used by vehicles or 2 m in height in any other case; means of access to a highway in connection with the provision of a hardstanding for vehicles and not affecting a trunk (classified) road; painting of exteriors, providing it is not in the nature of an advertisement.

In order to determine whether a proposed development will be likely to get planning permission when applied for, an application may be made for "outline planning permission". This is often made before land is bought or before costs of preparing detailed plans are incurred. If an outline planning permission is granted it will be subject to a condition that there should be a subsequent approval by the Local Planning Authority of any "reserved matters" relating to sitting, design and external appearance of buildings. Once an outline application is granted, the Local Planning Authority are committed to allowing the proposed development in some form or other, the only matters requiring subsequent approval by the Authority being such as are specifically reserved in the permission granted on the outline application. However, getting approval for reserved matters is not always straightforward and the recommendation of a mortgage advance should always be conditional upon full planning permission being granted.

Section 29 of the Act provides that the local Planning Authority may grant planning permission "subject to such conditions as they think fit". Section 30 specifically allows the Local Planning Authority to make conditions

(a) for regulating the development of any land under the control of the applicant, or requiring the carrying out of works on such land if these matters appear to the Authority to be expedient in relation to the development for which planning permission is given,

(b) for requiring the removal of buildings or works or the discontinuance of any use of land, authorised by the planning permission at the end of a specified period (in which case the permission is known as a "planning permission granted for a limited period"),

(c) for requiring that the building or other operations permitted by the planning permission shall be commenced not later than a specified date, in which case any operations commenced after that date will be operations commenced and carried out without planning permission.

In *Pyx Granite Co., Ltd.* v. *Ministry of Housing and Local Government*, Lord Denning said "although the Planning Authorities are given very wide powers to impose such conditions as they think fit, nevertheless the law says that those conditions, to be valid, must fairly and reasonably relate to the permitted development. The Planning Authority are not at liberty to use their powers for an ulterior object, however desirable that object may seem to them to be in the public interest."

Conditions which might affect the security of a property for mortgage purposes might include a condition limiting the occupation of a dwelling to persons whose employment was wholly or mainly in agriculture or forestry; or a condition requiring the carrying out of onerous and expensive works; or a planning permission granted for a limited period; or a planning permission with a condition that is *ultra vires* (that is imposed without jurisdiction) in which case the planning permission may be invalid.

Where a building is of special architectural or historic interest it is likely to have been listed by the Secretary of State and there will be an appropriate entry in the local land charges register. The Secretary of State may take into account not only the building itself but the extent to which its exterior contributes to the interest of a group of buildings of which it forms part and the desirability of preserving any feature, including an object or structure fixed to the building or forming part of the land. Where a building is not listed under the 1971 Act but nevertheless appears to the Local Planning Authority to be of special architectural or historic interest and it is threatened with demolition or alteration, the Local Planning Authority may serve on the owner and occupier of the building a "building preservation notice" which subjects the building, for a maximum six months, to the same protection and provisions as if it were listed. During this period of six months the Local Planning Authority may ask the Secretary of State to consider listing the building. It is an imprisonable offence to demolish, alter or extend a listed building without a written grant of consent known as "Listed building consent". As such consent is needed even for minor alterations to finishes, fittings, outbuildings, garden features, etc., it will be appreciated that to own a Listed building can be an onerous responsibility. In the event of damage to a Listed building, e.g. by storm or fire, there is a duty to restore it to its original condition and for this reason it is imperative that there be adequate insurance cover. A Local Authority may carry out works urgently necessary for the preservation of an unoccupied Listed building after giving seven days notice to the owner. They may also acquire compulsorily any building which is not being properly preserved, but not until at least one month after the service upon the owner of the building of a "repairs notice" specifying the work which is considered to be necessary for the proper preservation of the building.

A local Planning Authority may designate as a Conservation Area any part of their area which is of special architectural or historic interest, the character or appearance of which it is desirable to preserve or enhance. Once this is done, protection for unlisted buildings in the Conservation Area is available and the Local Authority can, with the consent of the Secretary of State, control the demolition of any unlisted building in the conservation area, in the interests of preserving the character of appearance of the area.

Section 87 of the 1971 Act allows that if irregular development has continued in being for a period of four years without getting itself subjected to an enforcement notice then such development becomes automatically permitted, provided the irregular development consists of

(a) the carrying out without planning permission of building, engineering, mining or other operations in, on, over or under land; or
(b) the failure to comply with any conditional limitations which relate to the carrying out of such operations and subject to which planning permission was granted for the development of the land; or
(c) the making without planning permission of a change of use of any building to use as a single dwelling house.

In respect of development involving a change of use (except change of use of a building to use as a single dwelling house) there is no time limit whatsoever on the service of an enforcement notice, provided that the change of use (or non-compliance with the condition or limitation in a planning permission relating to change of use) took place on or after 1st January, 1964.

Thus to ensure that a dwelling has the necessary planning permissions it is necessary to consider the following points:

In the case of a house or flat which has been built as a house or flat within the last four years (or is in course of construction or is to be built) is there a valid planning permission with no onerous conditions? A problem which occurs from time to time is that of the dwelling being built in a different location from that shown on the approved drawings. Hopefully, an astute valuer might pick this up.

In the case of a derelict shell of a house or of some existing building (e.g. a shop) having been converted into a single house within the last four years (or at present in course of conversion or to be converted) is there a valid planning permission with no onerous conditions?

Where two or more dwellings have been formed from a single dwelling or from any other building (or are in course of being so formed or are to be so formed) after 1st January, 1964, is there a valid planning permission without onerous conditions?

In the case of extensions, alterations or partial demolition of a dwelling or its outbuildings, or the erection of fences, construction of septic tanks, pavement crossings, access gates, etc., which have been carried out within the last four years (or are being carried out or are to be carried out) and which are not covered by the General Development Order, is there a valid planning permission without onerous conditions?

In the case of a building subject to a building preservation notice or a Listed building in which there have been extensions, alterations or partial demolition since the date of the building preservation notice or Listing of the building, is there a valid Listed building consent without onerous conditions?

In the case of demolition of an unlisted building in a conservation area where the Local Planning Authority have the consent of the Secretary of State to control demolition, has the approval of the Local Planning Authority been obtained?

The building society valuer will normally be able to find the information he requires about planning permissions for existing buildings by enquiries from the vendor or estate agent, or from his own local knowledge; if not the information is available at the Local Planning Authority. Where a mortgage application is for a dwelling to be built, or converted from some other building or formed by splitting an existing house into two or more dwellings, or for an extension or alteration to an existing property, it is helpful for building societies to arrange for copies of the statutory approvals to be sent to the valuer along with the drawings and estimates; otherwise it is a matter of relying on local knowledge or making appropriate enquiries.

4.4. Building Regulations

The Building Regulations 1976 are a complex legal document applying to the whole of England and Wales except for Inner London, where the system of control is based on bye-laws and the London Building Acts 1930–1939, although there is now a statutory provision which in due course will enable Building Regulations to be applied to Inner London. Work in Scotland is regulated by the Building Standards (Scotland) Regulations. Building Regulations are made by the Secretary of State for the Environment under powers in the Public Health Act 1936 and the Health and Safety at Work Act 1974, for the purposes of:

(a) securing the health, safety, welfare and convenience of people in or about buildings and of others who may be affected by buildings or matters connected with buildings,

(b) furthering the conservation of fuel and power,

(c) preventing waste, undue consumption, misuse or contamination of water.

Notice under the Building Regulations must be given to the Local Authority by any person wishing to

(a) erect a new building,

(b) make alterations to a building,

(c) extend the building,

(d) install works or fittings,

(e) make a material change of use of a building.

There are a limited number of exempted buildings as referred to in Section A5(1). By Section A5(2) eight classes of building enjoy partial exemption, and in some cases (including certain domestic outbuildings) notices may not be required. Notices are not required for the replacement of some heating appliances, for certain work carried out by area Gas Boards, nor for the replacement of existing sanitary fittings.

Building Regulations cover
Part A, interpretation in general,
Part B, materials,

Part C, preparation of site and resistance to moisture,
Part D, structural stability,
Part E, safety in fire,
Part F, thermal insulation,
Part G, sound insulation,
Part H, stairways, ramps, balustrades and vehicle barriers,
Part J, refuse disposal,
Part K, open space, ventilation and height of rooms,
Part L, chimneys, flue pipes, hearths and fireplace recesses,
Part M, heat-producing appliances and incinerators,
Part N, drainage, private sewers and cesspools,
Part P, sanitary conveniences.

Where a building is erected or work done contrary to the Regulations, the Local Authority may require its removal or alteration by serving notice on the building owner. Where work is required to be removed or altered and the building owner fails to comply with the notice, the Local Authority may remove the contravening work or execute the alterations themselves, charging the cost to the person concerned. Where a person contravenes or fails to comply with any provision in the Regulations (and in particular fails to give notice of intended works) he renders himself liable to prosecution.

Once a Building Regulation submission has been made, the Local Authority must give notice of approval or rejection of the plans within five weeks, unless the period is extended by written agreement. If no notice is received within five weeks, the plans are deemed to be approved. The approval lapses if the work is not commenced within a period of three years.

Notice to remove or alter contravening work may not be given after the expiration of twelve months from the date on which the work was completed. A notice cannot be served where the Local authority have passed the plans and the work has been carried out in accordance with the plans.

In the case of *Dutton* v. *Bognor Regis U.D.C.* (1971) it was held that the local Authority was liable for the negligence of its Building Inspector who had inspected the foundations of a house, when the foundations had subsequently proved defective. This decision was subsequently approved by the House of Lords in *Anns* v. *London Borough of Merton* (1977). Since these cases, Building Inspectors have tended to be very cautious in respect of approving foundations, often to the point of being pedantic. However, there is no doubt that in most cases this is in the interests of the home-owner and certainly in the interests of the building society, especially in cases of extensions which are not covered by N.H.B.C. guarantees.

Thus when considering an advance in connection with a property to be built, extended or altered, or to have fittings installed, the building society valuer should satisfy himself that Building Regulation approval has been obtained, or recommend that any advance be conditional upon such approval being obtained. When inspecting any new property, extensions, alterations or installation of fittings which have been completed for less than twelve months, the surveyor should satisfy himself that Building Regulation approval was obtained for the work and that it has been carried out in accordance with the Regulations.

Any contravention of the Building Regulations can have unfortunate consequences. From the point of view of the building society, contraventions which could result in major structural work being necessary or in rooms being unable to be used for their intended purpose will have a marked effect on the security provided by the property. Four hypothetical examples of such cases are given below.

Example

The foundations of a two-storey extension put in without approval and subsequently found to be of insufficient depth and founded on ground of inadequate bearing capacity. Costs of underpinning to comply with Building Regulations in the region £4,000.

Example

A lounge extended without approval at the back of a house to within two metres of the rear boundary, with large picture windows to take advantage of the magnificent view over open country. Regulation K1(3) requires a zone of owned open space outside the window of a habitable room extending not less than 3·6 m from the wall in which the window is built. If the home-owner is unable to purchase additional land or obtain a relaxation of the Regulation, he is faced with demolishing the rear 1·6 m of the extension or bricking up the picture windows and putting in mechanical ventilation!

Example

A barn was converted to residential use, without Building Regulation approval. It was subsequently found that the original foundations did not comply with current requirements, the

existing solid stone walls did not comply with Regulation
C8—weather resistance of external walls, nor with Regulation
F3—thermal insulation of walls. Costs of underpinning the
walls and constructing a new internal wall of insulating
blockwork in the region of £15,000.

Example

The intermediate floor of a three-storey terraced house failed to
conform with Regulation K8(1) in so far that the floor-to-ceiling
height was 2·2 m The ground and top floors complied exactly
with the Regulation, having a floor-to-ceiling height of 2·3 m If
a relaxation could not be obtained, it may be necessary to
raise the roof of the property and to raise the level of the
uppermost floor.

4.5. Tenancies—The Unwanted Occupier

The value of property held by a building society as security,
particularly in the case of residential property, is likely to be
reduced if the property is tenanted and the tenant has security
of tenure. Wurtzburg and Mills give details of a number of
cases and conclude that the crux of the matter, alike in
registered land and in unregistered land cases, is, "which came
first, the mortgage, or the entry into occupation by the person
whom it is desired to evict?". Where the tenancy was created
after the mortgage, the tenant can be evicted by the building
society in possession. However when the tenancy was created
first the occupier will have security of tenure. This may even be
so where the tenant has not gone into occupation of residential
property until after the mortgage but can show that his tenancy
was previously created by an estate owner or contracting
purchaser and duly protected in relation to unregistered land
by registration of an estate contract under the Land Charges Act
1925 or, in relation to registered land, by notice at the Land
Registry.

In cases of agricultural holdings or business premises, evic-
tion of an occupier by a mortgagee in possession will not be
possible once the occupier has asserted his rights to statutory
protection under the Agricultural Holdings Act 1948 or the
Landlord and Tenant Act 1954.

It should not be overlooked that by Section 54 of the Law of
Property Act 1925 tenancies of up to three years, at a rack rent,
can still be created by parole.

The unwanted occupier who causes the problem normally

achieves occupation, somehow or other, shortly before or at about the time of the mortgage. Wurtzburg and Mills conclude that the moral of it all is that the mortgagee should, at the time of creation of the mortgage, "have a good look at the property to see what persons are to be found in possession or occupation of it." This is something which the valuer will bear in mind whilst making his inspection and any indications of a tenancy or unwanted occupier in a dwelling being valued on a vacant possession basis should be drawn to the attention of the society, so that further enquiries can be made.

Chapter 5

The Valuation

Almost all the valuations with which the building society valuer is likely to be involved will be open market vacant possession valuations of private dwellings, using the comparative method. This applies to normal sales by private treaty or auction, sales to sitting tenants, sales "within the family", and Council house sales. New properties and properties being extended or improved will be valued in the same way but "subject to satisfactory completion". The only exception to valuations by the comparative method are likely to be the rare cases of tenanted property and properties on short leases.

To value successfully by the comparative method requires good up-to-date office records, preferably coupled with good local knowledge, for it often remains a mystery to the outsider as to why one district is so much more sought after than another apparently similar district only a short distance away.

Most of the major factors affecting the value of a property have been discussed in previous chapters. They include:

Type of property—detached, semi-detached, end-terraced, terraced, bungalow, two-storey, three-storey, ground floor flat, first floor flat, etc., maisonette. Back-to-back houses and basement flats will normally not be suitable for mortgage advance; nor will mobile or chalet homes. Some societies will not accept flats in blocks higher than four storeys and this may have an effect on value.

Tenure—freehold or leasehold. The length of the unexpired term of the lease and the amount of chief rent or ground rent may affect the value.

Arrangement—properties which are overshadowed or badly overlooked by others are likely to have reduced valuations. Properties opening directly off the street are likely to have a lower valuation than those with a front garden. Properties with access from a common courtyard or pedestrian alley will range from delightful and much sought-after mews houses to virtual slums.

Location—this factor is of major importance and is discussed in some detail in Chapter 2.7. above. It covers type of area, amenities and drawbacks in the area. Care is needed when a property is "out of its class".

Outlook and orientation—a property in which all main rooms face north is at an obvious disadvantage.

Character—properties with character are at a premium. In urban areas properties with a "country cottage" appearance are much sought after. Good conversions from such buildings as windmills, rural railway stations, barns, etc., usually command good prices, as do genuine period pieces such as Victorian gatehouses or Edwardian houses in the Art Nouveau style.

Accommodation—number, size, disposition and attractiveness of rooms; overall floor area.

Service installations—main services laid on or available; condition of service installations; means of heating.

Structural and decorative condition—extent and quality of fittings and fixtures—note that loose furnishings, light fittings which are not built into the structure and carpets (other than carpets which are adhesive fixed) cannot be included in the mortgage security.

Extent and condition of outbuildings, grounds and boundary walls/fences. Houses with a paddock, within easy reach of an urban centre, are at a premium.

Provision for motor vehicles—garages, garage space, car port, parking space within the curtilage, parking near-by; no convenient parking provision within the vicinity. Note that isolated garages on plots held on annual tenancies only cannot be included in the mortgage security.

Maintenance costs, running costs, rates, etc.—the larger and higher a property the more it is likely to cost to maintain and run, especially if the construction is complicated and includes decorative features and complicated roof constructions.

In the R.I.C.S. leaflet, "The Valuation of Residential Property—Conditions of Engagement", a valuation is defined as "the individual opinion of a valuer based on the relevant facts known to him", and "open market value" is defined as "the best price for which the property might reasonably be expected to be sold by private treaty at the date of the valuation assuming:-

(a) a willing seller;
(b) a reasonable period in which to negotiate the sale;
(c) that values will remain static during that period;
(d) that the property will be freely exposed to the market; and

(e) that no account will be taken of any higher price that might be paid by a purchaser with a special interest".

So far as a standard property, such as a two/three bedroomed semi-detached house with single garage and central heating, situated on an estate of perhaps 200 virtually identical houses, is concerned, it should be possible for the valuer to get the price right within a very few per cent, merely by comparison with office records and with prices recently obtained for other properties on the estate. However, when one comes to more individual properties, and particularly in the case of properties which are "one-offs" both in accomodation and location, it is far from easy, and it is here that the valuer's experience and local knowledge really do come into play. One method sometimes adopted by some valuers when dealing with unusual properties is to assess the maximum for which they think the property could sell and the minimum figure which it could be guaranteed to bring and to split the two figures to give a middle market valuation. When in doubt with an unusual property the valuer valuing for mortgage purposes should tend to play safe, or, if valuing up to a purchase price which he thinks may be on the high side, reduce the recommended percentage advance.

The property market is always changing and up-to-date office records are essential to establish trends. Office records may be supplemented with information from other sources and the valuer must keep his finger on the pulse of the property market in his area. Regular reference to local estate agent's lists, local newspapers and certain magazines will all assist, subject to the caution that asking prices are sometimes well above prices actually achieved.

The Incorporated Society of Valuers and Auctioneers has set up an Index of House Prices in connection with the magazine "Financial Weekly." This index was first published in April, 1979, and is to be up-dated quarterly. Eighty estate agents, from all over the country, were asked to value six specific properties in their locality at the beinning of 1978 and report at regular intervals on changes in value. The agents were required to select houses to provide a representative sample of the housing market falling into the following six categories:-

(1) Pre 1914 mid-terrace house, modernised with bathroom and inside lavatory, three bedrooms; a total of 800 sq ft of living space.
(2) Modern mid-terrace house with garage or parking space,

three bedrooms, two reception rooms or through living
room and totalling about 850 sq ft.
(3) Post war two-bedroomed flat with garage in purpose-built
block with 650 sq ft of living space.
(4) Mid-1930's semi-detached house with three bedrooms, a
garage and central heating. Around 900 sq ft in all.
(5) Modern detached, three-bedroomed house garage, cloakroom, central heating and a typical-sized garden for the
area. Living area of 1,100 sq ft.
(6) Modern detached four-bedroomed house with two bath-
rooms, two garages, cloakroom, two reception rooms,
central heating and typical garden for its size in the area.
A total of 1,500 sq ft of living space.

In addition to the house types, the index is broken down into
geographical areas, south-east, west, Midlands, north-west and
north-east. The index revealed an average increase of 18·3%
over the nine month period from April, 1978, to January, 1979,
ranging from the lowest rate of 12·4% in the north-east to
highest rate of 20·45% in the south-east. There were only
marginal differences between the rates of increase of various
types of property.

Several building societies also publish similar indices from
time to time.

The R.I.C.S. Guidance Note No. A3—"The Valuation of
Property Assets for Investment and as Security for Loans"
includes the following paragraph.

"Where a property is valued as a security for a loan, the basis
of valuation should normally be open market vlaue. Whilst the
valuer can be expected to provide an opinion as to the suitability of the security, it is for the lender to assess the risk involved
and express his assessment in fixing the terms of the loan such
as the percentage of value to be advanced, the provisions for
repayment of capital by instalments and the interest rate. The
Institution believes that it is not appropriate to value a property
to be used as a security on the basis of a forced sale".

Notwithstanding this, it is common in building society work
for valuers to make specific recommendations about the percentage of their valuations which may safely be advanced and
about the term of years of the mortgage. Some societies specifically request this information on their report forms: where this
is the case and there is no reason for a limited mortgage or term
these sections are best completed with the words "normal
maximum".

Other societies accept the position set out in the R.I.C.S. guidance note and require their valuers to categorise or classify the property only, leaving the percentage advance and term of years to be assessed by the building society. Typical classifications taken from a standard report form are as follows:-

A. Detached, semi-detached, or dwelling of character, very good construction, quality and situation and having all modern amenities.
B. Property of average quality and construction, with modern amenities, situate in an area of popular demand and requirement.
C. Property suitable for a limited advance term because of situation, age or unusual features or circumstances.
D. Recommend to be declined as not being a suitable security.

The B.S.I. "Model Valuation Form" includes the questions:
20. Recommended Advance

(a) What is the *maximum* amount you consider that the society should advance *on the security of this property alone?*
(b) What is the *maximum* term of years over which a loan should be made *on the security of this property alone?"*

However, the Research Group record that they were not unanimous in including these questions—the contrary view being that there are two separate and distinct assessments, to be made and that to mix them is dangerous: the valuer's task is to value the property and it is for the society to assess the adequacy of the security offered.

Open market value should always be used for building society valuations and not forced sale values.

Property held on Long Lease

If comparisons are to be made with freehold properties then in theory deductions should be made of the capitalised value of the ground rent. A similar deduction is appropriate in respect of chief rents on freehold properties. However, the theoretical deductions are not always borne out in practice.

Example

A detached house is held for the residue of 999 years with an annual ground rent of £50. Office records indicate that similar houses, held freehold and free from chief rent, are selling for £25,000.

	£	£
Valuation of similar freehold property by comparative method		25,000
Less Annual ground rent	50	
Y.P. at 10%	10	
		500
		£24,500

Property held on Short Lease

Any leasehold property where the unexpired term of the lease at the end of the mortgage term is less than 60 years needs special consideration.

Whilst it may be possible for the borrower to exercise his rights under the Leasehold Reform Act 1967, the valuer cannot presume that he will do this and thus when making a valuation for mortgage advance he must assume the worst case, namely that the landlord will succeed in getting possession at the end of the lease, in which case the valuation will be based on the nett rent which the property would command, using a dual rate (*i.e.* including a sinking fund) over the remainder of the lease. In this type of case the advance is often limited to two-thirds of the valuation, subject to the valuer checking that at any time during the term of the mortgage the outstanding portion of the advance does not exceed two-thirds of the valuation at that time.

Example

An applicant wishes to borrow £2,000 over ten years by way of mortgage to assist with the purchase of the 30 year residue of a 99 year lease on a house which has an annual ground rent of £5·00 and a rateable value of £85. Similar houses are letting at a nett rent of £6·00 per week (*i.e.* after deductions for rates, repairs, insurance and management) and have a vacant possession value of £7,000.

Present Valuation	£
Nett annual rental	312
Less ground rent	5
	307
Y.P. for 30 years at 6½% and say 2½% (tax at 35%)	10·00
Present value	3,070·00

(Note (1) The low percentage rate of return reflects the probability that the freehold can be purchased after five years at a
cost of £214, thus giving a considerable profit when compared
with the vacant possession value of £7,000—see Chapter **10.1.**
for worked example. If the property had been a flat or a house
with a rateable value above £400 in Greater London or £200
elsewhere, the property would be outside the scope of the
Leasehold Reform Act and hence a higher rate of return would
be appropriate (2) Rental assessments tend to be very hypothetical because of the variable nature of the deductions in respect
of repairs, etc.).

	£
Check Valution at end of proposed term	
Nett annual rental	312
Less ground rent	5
	307
Y.P. for 20 years at 6½% and 2½%	
(tax at 35%)	7·99
Value at end of term	£2,493·00

As the advance required is 65% of the present value and is
less than the value at the end of the term, this advance may be
safely recommended subject to there being no other adverse
factors.

Sitting Tenants

Where a sitting tenant is buying a property the valuation for
mortgage purposes must be the open market vacant possession
valuation. This will normally be considerably in excess of the
price being paid by the sitting tenant, and because the mortgage advance will therefore be well secured, some societies
will extend the advance to cover legal and surveyor's fees as
well as the purchase price. The actual price the sitting tenant
pays should be, by theoretical calculation, the mean of the
vacant possession value and the investment value of the
property. In practice however, tenants' desires to own and
improve their homes have often, in recent years, been such that
they have been prepared to pay more than the mean, and there
is no good reason why Societies should not support them in
this.

Council House Purchase

The position here is that the purchase is normally at an
advantageous price but there is usually a preemption clause
enabling the Council to buy back the property at the price they

sold it for if the purchaser sells the property within five years of purchase. In the circumstances the value of the property cannot exceed the purchase price. If the property is a house on a fairly small estate of well looked after properties with well tended gardens, the open market value would probably be much the same as for similar privately owned property, and the valuer will have few qualms, but if the property is set in the middle of a large unkempt estate he may well feel that the property would be virtually unsaleable if it came into the possession of the Society and in these circumstances will consider it necessary to advise against taking the property into mortgage. Recent experience of re-sales indicates that there is generally some resistance to paying a full comparable price.

Shop with Living Accommodation

In this case the valuation can be prepared on a rental basis with an appropriate percentage return depending upon the nature of the property, or alternatively by the comparative method. Nothing must be included for stock or business goodwill.

Example

	£
Investment method	
Shop 15 sq m at £20	300
Store 10 sq m at £5	50
Flat at £6 per week	312
Garage at 50p per week	26
Total rental	688
Y.P. in perp. at 12% say	8·3
Capital value	£5,660·00

Caution is needed in the assessment of the percentage return in view of the widespread closures of corner shops, as a result of changes in retail shopping patterns. As a result of these closures, a number of corner shops are being incorporated into living accommodation to form private dwellings only. Where this is proposed the valuation should be made on the basis of vacant possession value after completion of the necessary conversion work, less the costs of the work. The valuer should not overlook that planning permission and building regulation approvals will be needed. A mortgage might be recommended on the final value after conversion, with a retention amounting to the costs of the work being held back pending satisfactory completion.

Property Needing Major Improvements

Building societies are normally happy to encourage better use of the nation's housing stock by granting mortgages on properties which are capable of re-construction, re-furbishment, extension or improvement to give a satisfactory dwelling.

Where a property is being purchased with a view to major work being carried out, details of the proposed work—plans, specification, estimates and statutory approvals where applicable, should be submitted with the application, so that the valuer is fully aware of the proposals.

The valuer must ensure that the necessary statutory approvals are in order, that the proposals are sensible and that all necessary work is included for. This type of work is not covered by N.H.B.C. guarantees and if the work is complex or extensive, or if the house is one of considerable character, or if the valuer has doubts about the competence or conscientiousness of the builder, he should make it a condition of mortgage that the work will be looked after by a registered architect or chartered building surveyor.

The residual method of valuation is appropriate to determine the value of the property in its unimproved condition.

Example

	£
Vacant possession value on completion of work by comparison with other similar properties	16,000
Less coast of works as per builder's estimate	9,000
Value of property in unimproved condition	£7,000

The initial advance may be based on the £7,000 and the remainder of the monies advanced on completion or by means of stage payments. Some valuers, however, would make an arbitrary deduction of say 10%, thus recommending an advance on £6,300 in this case, as an incentive to the borrower to get the work done and in view of the difficulties of actually ensuring that the borrower does do the work.

Where a Local Authority improvement grant is being obtained, the amount of the grant should be deducted from the final value before calculating the amount of the percentage advance.

Example

		£
Vacant possession value on completion as above		16,000
Less improvement grant		2,500
Balance		13,500
Total mortgage advance offered on completion say 80%—in fact older-type properties generally qualify for 70% or 75% advance plus a further 15% with insurance indemnity.		0·8
		£10,800

Tenanted Residential Properties

It is unlikely that a building society valuer will be faced with valuing a tenanted property for mortgage. If he is the method will be to capitalise the estimated nett income by an appropriate figure of year's purchase based on rates varying from about 5% to 20% according to the type of security offered and the probability of a higher rent on conversion to a Regulated Tenancy where the property already qualifies. Alternatively the rate of return may reflect the possibility of a reversion to vacant possession value. The age and other circumstances of the tenant are important factors when considering the rate of return, but it must be kept in mind that a relative who has been resident in the property for six months prior to the death of the tenant has the right to continue the tenancy.

Where a tenanted property is in need of repair the costs of repairs must be deducted from the valuation.

Where a property is not up to the standard required for a Regulated Tenancy at a "fair rent" it will probably not have basic amenities and is unlikely to be suitable security for mortgage advance.

Example

A tenanted house with vacant possession value of £8,000, is let at a "fair rent" of £6 per week to a retired widower with no known relatives. There is an unsafe bulge to the apex of the gable wall, needing urgent attention.

Rent receivable £6 × 52		£312
Less outgoings:		
Rates	£60 @ 75p	45
Repairs		40
Insurance		20

Management	10%	31
Ground rent		2
		138
Nett income		174
Y.P. in perp. at 7% say		14·3
		2,488
Less estimated cost of rebuilding upper part of gable wall		1,000
Capital value say		£1,500

(Note: The low percentage return of 7% reflects the possibility of a reversion to vacant possession value of £8,000 in the not too distant future. If the tenant had an unmarried daughter who was also resident at the property the percentage return might well increase to 12·5% giving a capital value of say £400 only).

Land. Land does not provide an ideal security for mortgage. A vacant site may be of considerable value and cost nothing to maintain, but its value is probably of a speculative nature.

Where planning permission exists, the increased value attributable to the land because of it is of very dubious security for mortgage purposes as the following actual example illustrates.

Example

Outline planning permission was obtained to construct a hotel in the extensive grounds of a run-down Victorian house. On the strength of this planning permission the property was valued at £45,000 immediately prior to the collapse of the property market at the end of 1973. As a result of this valuation the property was taken into mortgage by a bank and a substantial sum advanced to the owners of the property. After the collapse of the property market no developer could be found to purchase the property, arrears accrued and the bank took possession, by which time the outline planning permission had expired and the local planning authority declined either to renew it or to grant approval for an alternative application for residential development. The mortgagee in possession was left with a property worth a mere £12,500.

Farms. Small farms situated near to urban areas and being sold with vacant possession are likely to attract purchasers who are not farmers and who will either put horses on the land or let it off to other near-by farms. These properties are usually valued by the comparative method as private dwellings, with an addition being made for the value of the land.

Larger farms and farms in rural areas are valued on a rental basis. Because of the complexities of farm valuations they should normally be carried out by valuers with experience in this field. The reader is referred to Chapter 11 in "Modern Methods of Valuation" for an outline of the various methods of valuing agricultural property.

Large Country Houses. The house at the centre of a landed estate is a difficult property to value. The value of stately homes may diminish according to grandeur, the lack of modern comforts, and the expenses of running the establishment. The impossibility of getting staff, coupled with the incidence of dry rot and Death Watch beetle ensure that such properties do not provide suitable security for a mortgage advance, indeed unless the property is purchased for use as a school, or nursing home, or for opening to view by the public, it may be reduced to having a demolition value only.

This is not the case with medium-sized country houses within a reasonable distance of London, which command very high prices indeed.

Commercial and Industrial Premises. Building societies do not normally make advances on this type of property and it is therefore considered in brief outline only.

The ordinary principles and methods of valuation apply. They are beyond the scope of this book and readers are referred to "Modern Methods of Valuation" for details of some methods in general use.

However, in valuation for mortgage certain factors have to be taken into account. In particular, as with all valuations for mortgage, the valuer must have regard to the mortgagee's position in relation to the property and to the remedies available to him in the event of default by the mortgagor, and that if it is necessary to realise the security in the future the sale price must be sufficient to cover the mortgage debt, arrears of interest and costs, if the mortgagee is not to suffer loss. To give effect to these factors the valuer should exclude the following items from his valuation:

(1) In the case of business premises, goodwill and stock.
(2) Anything which can easily be sold or removed by the mortgagor, such as timber or certain fittings.

(3) Future potential of a speculative nature which may never happen: this applies particularly to planning permission, which may expire before development has taken place and which may not be renewable.
(4) Likely capital expenditure on the property, such as accrued dilapidations or the anticipated costs of complying with legislation such as the Fire Precautions Act.
(5) Where the value of a property is largely dependant on the annual renewal of a licence the valuer must take into account the possibility of that licence not being renewed, in which case the proper valuation for mortgage purposes may well be the value of the property without the benefit of the licence. This is likely to be especially relevant in the case of certain types of licenced clubs where the justices' licence could be lost through mismanagement.

The valuation report should state the basis of the valuation and make specific reference to the items which have been excluded.

Besides making his valuation, the valuer will often advise his client on lending policy and express an opinion as to the maximum percentage of the valuation which can be safely advanced.

Factory premises are doubtful security, particularly if only suited to the needs of one trade which may be dependant on local industrial conditions or be very much affected by changes in the national economy. In these cases the valuer will consider it necessary to include in his valuation report an indication of the risks inherent in the nature of the security and may advise that if any advance is made at all, it should certainly be less than the normal two-thirds of the valuation.

Leaseholds, being in the nature of a wasting security, require care where the term is short. In any event care should be taken during the term of the mortgage to see that the property is kept in reasonable repair by the mortgagor, so as to avoid any risk of forfeiture.

Buildings for currently fashionable leisure pursuits are poor security because of the speed at which fashions change.

The property market fluctuates with periodic peaks and troughs. Whilst the valuation for mortgage will be on the basis of current open market prices at the date of valuation qualified as discussed above, if at that date the valuer knows the market to be "high" and supported by speculative buyers apparently willing to pay prices not justified by ordinary principles of investment return, then the valuer should make an assessment of the speculative content of the market price and, if at the time of valuation there is substantial ground for the valuer to know that the speculative content of his estimated market price will not or may well not be maintained in the future, or may well not be readily realisable on the forced sale of the property, this should be reflected in the guidance he gives to his client as to the percentage advance of the valuation which may safely be made.

Any valuer involved in the preparation of valuations of industrial or commercial premises for mortgage purposes would do well to read the lengthy judgment of Mr. Justice Gibson in *Corisand Investments Ltd.* v. *Druce & Co.* (1978) (248 E.G. 315, 407, 504) and also the judgment of Mr. Justice Watkins in the case of *Singer and Friedlander Ltd.* v. *John D. Wood & Company* (1977) (243 E.G. 212, 295).

Second Mortgages. A building society may not advance money on the primary security of a second mortgage, unless the prior mortgage is in favour of the society making the advance. Contributory mortgages may only be made when the borrower is a housing society.

However, where a society has taken a first mortgage on property as its primary security, it may take a second mortgage on other property as colateral security.

The building society valuer is quite likely to receive instructions from time to time from insurance companies and secondary banks to make valuations for second mortgage purposes. These valuations follow the same principles as for first mortgages and the valuer may wish to state the maximum percentage of the valuation which the sum of the monies advanced by the first and second mortgages together should not exceed. If the second mortgagor subsequently chooses to ignore that advice then the risk is his.

Housing Societies. The Housing Act 1964 allows building societies to advance monies to housing societies on the primary security of a contributory mortgage.

Housing societies build houses and flats for letting: they also acquire and refurbish existing premises for letting.

Housing society developments should be valued on an investment basis, in the same way as any other tenanted property. Before the scheme comes to the building society surveyor, the anticipated rents receivable will already have been assessed by the Housing Society and also by the District

Valuer. If the valuer considers that the estimated rental figures are too high, he should not hesitate to use lower figures.

The various factors relevant to the valuation of houses or flats, as discussed in other chapters, are equally applicable to Housing Society developments. In addition care is needed where there is a danger that a large development with properties to let may flood the market, especially in cases of flats in an area where flats are not common.

The points set out in Chapter 8 in connection with owner-occupied flats are largely relevant to Housing Society developments.

Housing Societies include the following:

(a) Self-build societies. These are formed by groups of persons who intend to build houses for themselves with their own hands. The houses are initially the property of the society, but equitable arrangements are made whereunder the members acquire the houses and become owner-occupiers. Care is needed to ensure that adequate finance to complete this scheme is available: also that there is adequate professional knowledge available to the members—in this respect a condition that the work is supervised by a chartered architect would be appropriate.

(b) Cost-rent societies catering for people not in need of subsidised housing but who for one reason or another are unable or unwilling to become owner-occupiers.

(c) Co-ownership societies whose members (and no one else) are themselves the occupiers of the houses provided and who are eligible for the benefits of the Mortgage Option Scheme. Somewhat complicated rules ensure that when a member no longer wishes to occupy a house belonging to the society an equitable financial arrangement is made with him (which takes into account the length of the period he has been in occupation and any substantial appreciation in the value of the property) and with the new member who takes his place.

(d) Housing Co-operatives, which are similar to co-ownership societies, but membership is not necessarily confined to the occupiers.

Chapter 6

The Insurance Valuation

Most building society valuation report forms include space for a "recommended insurance cover". The purpose of this is to enable the society, through whom the property is usually insured as a condition of mortgage, to know what the property should be insured for, and thus to ensure that their security is not impaired in the event of fire, storm or other damage. At the same time the valuation enables the society to advise the borrower and so protect him from the risks of under-insurance.

Most standard household insurance policies provide cover against loss or damage to the buildings of "the private dwelling house, being brick, stone or concrete built and roofed with slates, tiles, metal or concrete" and its domestic outbuildings, fixtures and fittings, walls, gates and fences all on the same premises, together with damage for which the insured is responsible to water, oil, gas, sewage and drainpipes, underground telephone and electricity cables extending from the buildings to the public mains; plus architects' and surveyors' fees not exceeding those recommended by the Royal Institute of British Architects and the Royal Institution of Chartered Surveyors and necessarily incurred in the re-instatement of the buildings (but not for preparing any claims) and the reasonable additional cost of alternative accommodation when the private dwelling is uninhabitable due to an insured event but only for the necessary re-instatement period (and the total amount payable in any one period of insurance for alternative accommodation will not exceed 10% of the sum insured). Some policies also include terraces, drives and paths, but damage to garden plants is not normally included. Property which is constructed of combustible materials such as walls of timber, or roof of felt or thatch is likely to need an endorsement to a standard policy and may attract a higher premium. It is therefore important that the surveyor should draw attention to these cases in his report. Where only a small proportion of the walls or roof are of combustible materials, e.g., a weatherboarded panel or felted dormer, it is not customary for the insurers to take these into consideration, and it is probably not necessary for the surveyor to draw specific attention to such details, although they may have been referred to in the descriptive section of the report. Fixtures and fittings are defined in the standard text-books on the law of property, where cases are cited: they normally include kitchen fittings (including hob and cooker units where these are built in), bathroom fittings, fireplaces, heating fixtures (including storage heaters where these are permanently wired in) and built-in furniture. Panelling may be included, depending on its nature. Tapestries, carpets, curtains, light fittings (unless integral with the fabric) are not included. The underground pipes and cables are covered for accidental damage only, and only so far as the insured is responsible for them. Outbuildings on a separate plot, away from the house, as garages often are, will probably not be covered under the normal standard policy, and in these cases the surveyor should draw specific attention to the separate outbuilding.

The insured events are usually as follows:

Fire, lightning and explosion.
Riot, civil commotion, strikes, labour disturbances or malicious persons (but not in Ireland where there may be other provisions).
Aircraft and other aerial devices or articles dropped therefrom.
Earthquake.
Theft or any attempt thereat.
Storm, tempest and flood (but not excluding damage to fences and gates).
Bursting or overflowing of water tanks, apparatus or pipes.
Frost damage (but with many exclusions).
Impact by road or rail vehicles or animals.
Wreckage or collapse of aerials.
Leakage of oil from heating installations.
Subsidence of the site on which the property insured stands or land belonging thereto or landslip but not to walls, terraces, drives, paths, gates, and fence unless these are destroyed or damaged by the same cause and at the same time, and normally subject to an excess equivalent of 3% of the reinstatement value. Some policies also include for damage by falling trees. Cover for bursts, oil leakage, malicious damage or theft is generally excluded when a dwelling is left insufficiently furnished for full habitation for a period exceeding 30 days.

The only way of computing the cost of rebuilding with any

reasonable accuracy is to take off approximate quantities and price them out. This is a time-consuming exercise which clearly cannot be done for each house valued for a building society. However, it is important that the building society valuer has rates per square metre (or per square foot) for typical houses which are based on approximate quantities and which can be applied as appropriate. These basic rates are available in the "Guide to House Rebuilding Costs for Insurance Valuation" prepared on behalf of the British Insurance Association by the Building Cost Information Service of the Royal Institution of Chartered Surveyors, first published in November, 1978. This publication must surely be welcomed by all building society valuers and is an indispensable guide for the average valuer, who does not have elemental bills of approximate quantities for various house types readily available within his office. It is important to appreciate that the figures given are a guide only, for typical house types, and the valuer must exercise his skill and judgment on each occasion to adjust the basic figures, up or down as appropriate, in the light of materials used, constructional details, site conditions and other factors. The elemental breakdowns and quality specifications given in the appendices to the Guide will assist the valuer in making his adjustments to the basic figures.

Guidance is given on rebuilding costs for typical brick-built houses in the United Kingdom expressed in pounds per square metre and pounds per square foot of gross external area. Figures are given in tables for:

Four regional groups—(1) London
(2) South-East England and Scotland
(3) Wales, the North-West, Yorkshire and Humberside
(4) Northern England, East Anglia, the South-West, East and West Midlands and Northern Ireland.

Five house-types—
(1) Detached house
(2) Semi-detached house
(3) Terraced house
(4) Bungalow
(5) Semi-detached bungalow

Three age bands—
(1) 1945 to date
(2) 1920–1945
(3) Pre 1920

Three sizes—
(1) Small

                                    (2) Medium
                                    (3) Large
            Three quality bands—   (1) Basic
                                    (2) Good
                                    (3) Excellent

Notes on the application of the rates given in the Guide are as follows:

Floor Areas. Alternative tables are given for metric and Imperial dimensions. It is most important to note that the areas used are measured externally, in contrast to standard construction industry practice, which uses measurements to internal faces of external walls. The difference between the floor areas resulting from the use of the two methods usually falls in the range 10–15%.

Additional Storeys and Attics. A figure equivalent to 75% of the appropriate rate is suggested for third floors and attics, with areas having a ceiling height of less than 1·5m being ignored.

Basements and Cellars. The Guide recommends that the full rate applicable to the remainder of the property should be applied to basements.

Garages. Integral garages are included with the gross floor area of the house and priced at the appropriate cost per unit area from the tables. Additional figures are given for attached or detached garages of different sizes, types and qualities.

External Works. Nothing is included for external works such as swimming pools, walls, fences or drainage and the surveyor must make an appropriate addition for these.

Base Date. Figures given in the first edition of the Guide are at July, 1978, levels. It is intended that the Guide will be up-dated annually and that in between B.C.I.S. quarterly indices of rebuilding costs can be used to up-date the figures.

Temporary Works. Allowances are made for temporarily making safe the damaged structure and in the case of attached houses for half the cost of replacing party walls and for the cost of protecting adjoining structures.

Fees. Allowance is made for professional fees at an average figure of 12%.

V.A.T. No allowance is made for V.A.T., presumably on the grounds that in the event of total or near total loss the work will be of a new nature and thus not subject to V.A.T.

Inflation. No allowance is made for inflation during the currency of the policy or in any subsequent period before rebuilding is completed. This is on the grounds that most policies are now index-linked, which, in the words of the B.I.A. leaflet, "A Guide to Buildings Insurance for the Home-owner", simply means "that your sum insured is changed automatically whenever there is a movement in the average cost of house building. Usually there is no charge for any increase between renewal dates". If a policy is not index-linked a suitable allowance must be made for inflation. Policies effected through building societies are normally index-linked and so there will be no need for the valuer to make an addition for this.

Quality. Costs are calculated for three qualities—basic, good and excellent. Specification notes and elemental breakdowns are given, but in some cases the surveyor will need to interpolate between the figures or to extrapolate beyond them.

Construction. The figures given relate to houses constructed mainly of brick, and the elemental rates will need adjustment for houses with other forms of construction such as stone.

Demolition. Demolition and site clearance are included for.

Central Heating. Central heating is included for in all houses except the basic quality pre-1920 and the basic smaller medium sized 1920–45 properties.

Variables. Whilst the Guide lists 468 individuals costs, it makes the point that every house has its own unique characteristics and that many variables combine to produce the specific rebuilding costs of a particular property. It is up to the surveyor to make such adjustments to the basic rates as he deems appropriate in each instance.

Building Standards. It is assumed that the rebuilding will be to the original design but in modern materials, using modern techniques, to a standard equal to the existing property and in accordance with current Building Regulations and other statutory requirements.

Exclusions. Houses which are not of modern materials and are required to be reinstated exactly, or which have special architectural features which have to be reinstated, are outside the scope of the Guide, which advises that a professional valuation is essential for such properties. Nor are the costs applicable to houses of a size greater than those set out in tables 9 and 10 of the Guide.

Example

Recommend the insurance cover for a semi-detached house in the North-West of England built in 1925 with good quality construction and fittings and extending to 62·5 sq m on each of two floors plus the same area in an attic storey and with a basement extending to 23 sq m (all measured externally). The house has an attached single brick garage of good construction and a brick boundary wall to the front garden. The valuation is required in July, 1978, and the policy is index-linked.

Area on each floor		62·5 sq m
No. of Floors		× 2
		125 sq m
Appropriate rate per sq m from table 3 of B.C.I.S. Guide (using table 9 to determine size)	£	256
Total		32,000
Add for attic storey of 62·5 sq m at 75% of £256 per sq m		12,000
Add for basement of 23 sq m at £256 per sq m		5,888
Add for attached single garage of good standard from table 13		2,100
Add estimated cost of outbuildings, walls and fences		400
Total based on July, 1978, rates		£52,388

If the figure needs to be that at a later date, the basic figure may be multiplied by the appropriate factor from the B.C.I.S. quarterly index of rebuilding costs.

In the case of houses which do not fall within the B.C.I.S. range, such as very large houses, houses with special architectural features, houses which are not built of modern materials and must be reinstated as they are, and Listed buildings, the only reliable way to calculate an insurance valuation is for approximate quantities to be prepared on an elemental basis, in the same way in which B.C.I.S. have done for standard houses. This is a skilled and lengthy business and certainly beyond the scope of the normal building society survey. It is the writer's opinion that in cases of this sort the valuer should explain the position and recommend that it be a requirement of mortgage advance that the applicant has the property professionally valued for insurance purposes by a chartered quantity surveyor or building surveyor who is experienced in this type of work.

It will be appreciated that valuations for insurance bear little relationship to market values. Normally they will be higher, especially in the case of larger old houses in inner urban areas where the insurance value is sometimes as much as eight or more times the market value. Even with fairly new houses the insurance valuation can be above the market value as the costs of a "one-off" are considerably in excess of the costs of building a lot of similar houses on a large estate. Occasionally the insurance valuation will be lower than the market value, generally in areas where land values are high.

A building society will normally require its borrowers to insure their property at the figures based on re-building costs as advised by the society's valuers. It is generally not in the borrower's interests to under-insure and it should not be overlooked that adjoining owners may have rights of support, the Local Authority may bring proceedings in the case of unsafe buildings, and in the case of leasehold property the lease will normally include a clause requiring the property to be reinstated. Total losses may seem inconceivable to the insured but the writer is aware of several cases where they have occurred.

On the other hand there are likely to be a small number of cases where it will be inappropriate to insure for the full re-building costs. These are likely to be large older properties with a low market value but very high re-building costs. The argument is that household policies are not subject to average and it is unlikely that an entire house will be destroyed and, even if it is, provided the insured gets enough money to buy another similar house, he will be adequately compensated. Validity has been given to this argument by the Appeal Court decision in the case of *Leppard v. Excess Insurance Co. Ltd.* (1979 250 EG 751; 123 SJ 182, which confirmed the insurer's right under a home buildings policy to pay not the cost of reinstating the property but only its market value which was some thousands of pounds less, although premium had been paid for the former. However, this is not a typical case as: the building, a cottage, was up for sale, had been empty since 1972 and the cost of reinstatement was more than double the market value that the building would have after reinstatement.

Some insurances are prepared to make special terms for policy holders with properties of low market value but whose size and type are such that they have a very large reinstatement cost. They will probably take some point between market value and re-building cost as the sum insured, charge the normal full rate on that sum but fix the market value plus certain expenses as the maximum payment they will make. The policyholder is covered for the "run of the mill" small claim but has to accept that he may have what insurers call "a constructive total loss" and have to move if the cost of repairing his part-damaged home is around the sum insured.

In cases of this type the building society valuer should state the re-building costs coupled with the advice that the case may be an appropriate one for special insurance arrangements. In such circumstances the building society will normally agree to some special arrangments being made between the borrower and the insurers. This is not likely to be appropriate in the case of a "Listed" building, and caution is needed in the cases of leasehold buildings where there is a clause in the lease requiring the building to be insured for the full reinstatement cost. The building society valuer should never take it upon himself to recommend a specific figure for insurance cover which is less than the re-building cost—the decision to insure for less than the re-building cost is a matter between the insured, the insurers and the building society.

Another occasion when the insurance cover may possibly be reduced is when a private dwelling has extensive out-buildings which are not in general use and which do not make a significant difference to the market value of the property, for example, former farm buildings. In cases of this type the building society valuer should give an insurance valuation for the house and main outbuildings and a separate figure for the secondary outbuildings, coupled with a recommendation that if the borrower wishes there is no need for the society to insist that the secondary outbuildings are insured.

Chapter 7

The Plan

Most building societies require a block plan, or location plan, of the property to be forwarded with the report. This plan usually has to be drawn on a separate sheet provided by the society, often of tracing paper. In other cases the plan has to be drawn in a space provided on the main report form itself. This latter arrangement is inconvenient as it means the plan cannot be drawn at the same time as the report is being typed and it is difficult to erase if a mistake is made. A separate sheet of tracing paper is the best; it allows copying by photo-copier or dye-line machine; plans can be traced directly from builders' layouts or Ordnance Survey sheets when necessary, or the printed piece of tracing paper can be used as an overlay to an extract from an Ordnance Survey sheet, thus allowing the relevant section of the Ordnance sheet to be reproduced with the appropriate titling, etc. When the plan is subsequently passed to the solicitor, comparison with other plans is facilitated by being able to use the tracing paper as an overlay—even if scales are different, the angles should still be the same.

The purpose of the plan is to enable the solicitors acting for the society, who normally never see the property, to ensure that they are conveying the right house, and incidentally to check that the valuer has surveyed the right house. It is not unknown for the wrong house to have been surveyed, especially where two adjacent properties are both up for sale through the same agent; or on a new estate where there are no road names or house numbers.

Another reason for the plan is to enable the solicitor to check that the boundaries shown on the deeds or Land Registry certificate coincide with those which exist on site. This is not always the case; the writer has recently dealt with a case where prior to conveyance a vendor encroached several yards on to a field at the rear of the house and constructed a vehicular access to his property, thus increasing its value by several thousand pounds; some twelve months after completion of the sale the adjoining landowner noticed the encroachment and commenced proceedings to recover his land!

Information to be shown on the plan should include the

house itself, permanent outbuildings, site boundaries, adjacent roads and/or footpaths (noting if unmade), the main dimensions of the site (frontage and depth), number and/or name of the house and adjoining houses, any private access roads, rights of way of others over the property (e.g. shared drives), any easements for private water supply, sewers or septic tanks, etc., located on land not in the ownership of the vendor, northpoint and a note of the scale. Undefined boundaries should be so marked and land known to be held on short tenure should be clearly differentiated from land which is freehold or long leasehold.

The most appropriate scale for the plan is 1/500th. This scale has the advantage that it is in common use in both Imperial and metric units and is the normal scale for builders' layouts for new developments. The plot will normally be measured on site and drawn up in the office. In cases of new houses where site boundaries are not defined at the time of survey the plan is traced from the builder's layout and should be endorsed "Site boundaries are not yet defined. This plan has been traced from the builders' layout." Dimensions are best not shown in these cases. The plan can be confirmed later at the time of the final inspection on completion of the property.

Where the property has fairly extensive grounds, the plan will not fit on the sheet provided at 1/500th scale and in these cases 1/1250 or, where there are several acres, 1/2500 is appropriate. Where the grounds are extensive, perhaps extending to many acres, the task of physically measuring the site is beyond the scope of the building society survey and the valuer will trace or photo-copy the appropriate extract from the Ordnance sheet and superimpose the information listed above. The main dimensions, e.g. road frontages, can be measured on site as a check. Often, in cases of larger properties, the vendor's agent includes an extract of the Ordnance Survey plan with the particulars of sale.

For flats the plan needs to show the particular flat in question, located and dimensioned within the outline of the whole block. Common stairs and/or lift serving the flat should be shown, together with the extent of the external common areas in appropriate cases. The floor on which the flat is situated should be clearly indicated on the plan. Again 1/500th is an appropriate scale or, for larger blocks, an extract from the Ordnance Survey sheet.

Plans are best drawn and lettered in black drawing ink: this reads and prints clearly and gives a smart appearance. Drawing is best done on a drawing board with tee square and set square, or drafting machine. Rapidograph or similar drawing pens are in general use: these facilitate the use of thicker lines for the outline of the actual house itself. The boundaries should be marked in red—traditionally this was done with red drawing ink, nowadays most offices use a red felt-tip pen. Brown is an appropriate colour for rights of way, blue for easements and green for areas of land held on short lease: where part of one house extends above or beneath part of an adjoining house this must be noted on the drawing and the area in question can be coloured to draw attention to it. The north point, scale and name of the surveyor's firm can most easily be added by rubber stamps.

In order to trace or photo-copy Ordnance Survey maps it is necessary to have a licence which is available, subject to payment of the appropriate fee, from the Director of the Ordnance Survey at Southampton. Some valuers will have complete sets of Ordnance Survey sheets for their area. Those in major urban centres will have the advantage of a main Ordnance Survey dealer who holds up-to-date negatives of all the plans in his area and can run off prints on request. Smaller local dealers hold more limited stocks of their immediate area. Local Authorities also hold negatives of Ordnance Survey sheets and traditionally have been prepared to provide extract copies of plans on payment of a small fee, but they are under pressure from the Ordnance Survey department to do this only for private individuals and not for professional offices. Libraries often hold Ordnance Survey sheets for their area but in some districts there is a reluctance to allow them to be traced. All tracings or photocopies from Ordnance Survey sheets will need to have the scale and north point marked on them and in addition the terms of the licence to reproduce from Ordnance sheets requires that each copy should also bear the name of the firm preparing it, the date and the words "Reproduced from/ based upon the Ordnance Survey map with the sanction of the controller of H.M. Stationery Office, Crown copyright reserved".

All plans sent out by the valuer's office should be signed and an office copy kept.

However, before the plan can be drawn, site measurements must be taken, or, if the Ordnance Survey sheet is being used, boundaries must be checked on site. Measurements are taken to the actual boundaries as defined on site, even though the legal boundary may in fact extend beyond, e.g., the centre of an adjacent road. In the case of registered land the half of the highway is in fact excluded from the registration of the title of the adjoining land if the highway has been adopted by the Local Authority. It is generally best to sketch the entire plan first and then take the measurements, relating them to the fixed points provided by the house itself. The overall site dimensions are best taken by tape, and the use of running dimensions is the most accurate method, although it can lead to confusion if the plan is not being drawn by the person who took the measurements. Most valuers will be working single-handed and even if they have an assistant it will generally be more economical in terms of time for the valuer to deal with the report itself whilst his assistant prepares the plan. Single-handed working requires the use of a surveyor's dart or pin to secure the end of the tape. Shorter dimensions are more easily taken with a 2 m or 6 ft folding staff. When the site is rectangular the job is easy but not so when it is irregular, in which case, starting from the fixed points of the corners of the house (or some other fixed points) it is necessary to fix all the points at which the boundaries change direction, by means of triangulation, *i.e.*, by taking two measurements to each of these points from different fixed points and then plotting the boundaries on the plan, using a pair of compasses. For curving or irregular lengths of boundary it is necessary to set up a string line in a recorded fixed position and to measure 90° offsets from this line to the boundary at appropriate intervals. Where land slopes, it is the horizontal dimension that is required to be determined, and on a steeply sloping site this may involve measuring a distance in a series of short horizontal lengths with the assistance of a 2 m ranging rod (of the type which splits into two pieces for ease of carrying). Measurements must be taken of the widths of all unmade roads adjacent to the site so that the potential liability for paving charges can be calculated. North must be determined either by the local knowledge of the valuer, or by reference to a map or by use of a compass.

When checking boundaries against an Ordnance Survey map any differences between the map and the actual boundary on site should be noted, bearing in mind that an encroachment upon neighbouring land which lasts for twelve years (more in exceptional cases) and which fulfils the requirements of the Limitation Act 1939 for adverse possession inconsistent with the owner's title, completely extinguishes the former owner's right to the land (unless the title is registered). Where the title of the land concerned is registered, the former owner remains registered proprietor, holding in trust for the squatter (Land Registration Act 1925 s.75). Thus a purchaser of registered land cannot assume that all the land included in the registered title is occupied, or even beneficially owned, by the registered proprietor and this is another reason for the importance of the surveyor's plan.

Some societies require the site area to be calculated and stated in the report: this is best done after the plan is drawn. Again a rectangular plan is easy but an irregular one must be split into triangles and the area of each calculated by scaling and using the formula, area of triangle = half base × perpendicular height.

There are certain presumptions about boundaries which the surveyor needs to know when doing his survey in order to measure to the correct points.

Brick boundary walls and close-boarded fences are generally built so that the piers and upright supports protrude into the land of the owner of the wall or fence. Accordingly, the mode of construction of this type of wall or fence is *prima facie* (but not exclusive) evidence of its ownership, and the boundary is normally the outside face of the wall or fence.

Where two pieces of land are separated by an artificial ditch along the side of a bank, with or without a hedge or fence on it, there is a presumption that the boundary is along the edge of the ditch farthest from the bank. This arises from the assumption that the landowner digs his drainage ditch on the extreme edge of his property and throws up the earth on to his own side of the ditch to avoid committing a trespass against his neighbour, so forming the bank upon which he plants a hedge or erects a fence.

Where a boundary is marked by a hedge it is normal practice to take the centre line of the hedge as the boundary.

In the case of non-tidal rivers, the boundary of the adjoining or riparian lands is presumed to be in the centre of the stream. If there are gradual, imperceptible accretions to either bank in the ordinary course of nature, the additional land belongs to that riparian owner, and the boundary in the centre of the stream is automatically adjusted, even though the original boundary may still be ascertainable. If, however, the river suddenly completely changes its course, the boundary remains where it was immediately before the diversion. Where there is evidence that the river and its bed belong to some person other than the owners of the banks, the boundary is the waterline when the river is in its natural state, disregarding seasonal fluctuations.

The bed of a river where it is tidal *prima facie* belongs to the Crown and continues to do so although the river may gradually change course. The boundary on each side is medium high water.

The boundary between the sea shore and the adjoining land is presumed to be the line of medium high tide between the ordinary spring and neap tides. If the medium high tide line moves, the boundary of land described as bounded by the sea shore moves with it. Imperceptible accretions to the shore, as the sea recedes, are the property of the owner of the land to which they are attached.

Where a house is conveyed there is a presumption that it passes in its entirety including projecting eaves and footings (although not shown on the plan) but not the air space between them (*Truckell* v. *Stock* 1957 1 W.L.R. 161). Walls which are shared by two properties (e.g. those between semi-detached or terraced houses) may belong to one of the adjoining houses exclusively if there is clear evidence that the wall is on one side of the boundary line. It is usual, however, for these to be party walls and in the absence of contrary evidence there is the presumption that the boundary runs down the middle of the wall, each half being owned by the landowner adjoining it. Where a boundary wall is built exclusively on the land of one owner it belongs to him in the absence of agreement to the contrary. The adjoining owner may acquire rights over it by agreement or, where there has been use as a right for twenty years, by prescription. Long use of a wall as part of a building on his land does not give the adjoining owner title to the wall but almost certainly will give an easement of support for the roof.

Basements of premises adjoining streets sometimes extend under the street. Attention should be drawn to such cases on the valuer's plan. Although roads adopted by the Local Authority are excluded from registered titles, basements under them will be included in the registration if the position is made clear to the Land Registry.

Sometimes boundaries are entirely undefined and the valuer has to rely on the verbal advice of the vendor or agent as to where the boundaries are. This should be clearly drawn to the attention of the solicitor by differentiating the undefined land from the remainder on the valuer's plan.

Some societies do not ask for a plan at all. It is interesting to note in this respect that the BSI Research Group, in "Mortgage Lending Procedure—A model", suggest that a block plan need only be prepared if the property is:

(a) about to be built, or under construction, or

(b) already built, but on an irregular-shaped site *provided* that where no plan is prepared the report contains the dimensions—frontage and depth—of the site.

In addition to the plan some societies call for a photograph of the property. This may be of some use to the local branch manager of the society in discussing the case with the applicant, but is probably not worth the additional time, trouble and expense which it entails. Where a photograph is asked for, it is often possible to get one from the selling agent and for other cases the valuer must equip himself with an instant camera, taking care to mark the reverse of the photograph with the address of the property as soon as he has taken it!

Chapter 8

Flats

8.1. Types of Flats

Flats present a different range of problems to the valuer. Prior to the last 25 years or so it was general for flats to be let on weekly or monthly tenancies. Nowadays, largely to avoid the restrictions of the Rent Act, it is normal for any self-contained flat in reasonable order which becomes vacant to be sold freehold or, more generally, to be let for a term of years at a ground rent with an initial premium. Virtually all the new flats which have been built during the last 25 years have been built for sale, apart from those built by Local Authorities or Housing Associations.

Where flats are not self-contained, as is the case with many houses in multiple occupation, it is common for sanitary facilities, often very limited, to be shared. This type of arrangement is not uncommon in the earlier conversions of large Victorian houses in inner urban areas. It is generally recognised that this type of "flat" does not lend itself to disposal by way of sale or long lease and that it is not suitable security for mortgage advance, because of the problems associated with the management of common facilities.

So far as self–contained flats are concerned, there are a wide variety of types which the surveyor may encounter. The following are among the main categories.

The Traditional Scottish Tenement. This dates from the 16th century in Edinburgh and may be up to ten storeys in height. Scottish law is rather different from English law and Scotland has a much longer history of flats with owner-occupiers, these flats being held on "feu". In Scottish tenement buildings where each flat is owned separately, each owner has a common interest in the property "outwith" his own, so far as is necessary for support and shelter. Thus, although the external walls of each property belong to individual owners, they may not interfere with them in such a way as to endanger the other properties. The rule has become established that each owner owns his floors and ceilings as far as the midpoint of the joists, but must not interfere with them in such a way as to weaken his neighbour's floor or ceiling. It is general in Scotland that the roof over tenement property belongs to the owner of the top storey, but all properties in the building have a common interest in seeing that it is properly maintained and they may compel the owner to keep it in repair or to refrain from damaging it. Stairs and passages are maintained by all whose premises they form an access to, as they are deemed to be "common property".

Purpose-built Two-storey Flats. This type of property normally has one flat on the ground floor and a second flat on the first floor, each with its own separate entrance at ground level. These pairs of flats may be semi-detached or in terraces. They are often known as maisonettes, although in some areas this term is used to describe a flat with accommodation on two floors. Examples of this type of property are found in late Victorian developments. From the outside they appear very like houses, apart from having adjoining front doors. Often the front garden goes with the ground floor flat and the back garden with the upper flat, from which there may be a second staircase to the garden. Sometimes the lessee of the first floor flat is responsible for the upkeep of the roof, while the lessee of the ground floor flat is responsible for the upkeep of the drainage system. The lessee of the ground floor flat may be responsible for the repair and maintenance of the main walls to first floor level, with the lessee of the first floor flat responsible above the ground floor. There may be a cold water storage tank in the roof serving both units. Most of the examples of this type of property from the inter-war years are Council properties. During the last 20 years or so a number of new developments have incorporated this type of dwelling. The maintenance of the main structure and shared services may be split between the two dwellings as described above or with each being responsible for 50%. In either case the presence of defects affecting the main structure or common services could have a serious effect on the valuation or suitability for mortgage. Thus the surveyor's inspection must extend beyond the flat being surveyed to the whole of the exterior of the property.

Conversions of Larger Houses into Flats. These will be mainly Georgian or Victorian houses, with occasional examples from earlier or later periods. They may be terraced, semi-detached or detached houses and converted into two or several flats. These units may be single-floor flats, two-floor maisonettes or some other arrangement. Besides the interior of the flat the surveyor will need to assess the condition of the main structural walls, the roofs and the drainage, etc. There may well be evidence that the main structure is showing signs of its age. The quality of the conversion work may be poor. In particular noise between flats can be a problem.

Flats and Maisonettes above Commercial Property. This category will include flats or two-storey maisonettes above shops, with separate stairs from street level, and penthouse flats above office premises. As with all other surveys of flats, it is not adequate to restrict the survey merely to the flat itself. In considering flats above commercial property the likely uses to which the commercial property could be put must be considered. A flat located above a draper's shop might be totally unsaleable if the use of the shop changes to a fishmonger, for example. Flats situated above poor secondary commercial investments must be considered very poor security for mortgage purposes.

Purpose-Built Blocks of Flats, erected prior to 1914. Flats from this period vary from stark blocks built for manual workers in the cities to large pretentious structures housing what are now often known as "mansion flats". The former were often built as cheaply as possible and, notwithstanding the fact that conversions to modern standards may have been carried out, timber ground floors may be affected by damp and inadequate ventilation, walls may suffer rising damp and the flat roofs are likely to be in a patched condition. Common parts are likely to be stark and gloomy and there may be basement flats whose accommodation is completely sub-standard. The middle range of Victorian flat developments are likely to be much superior in appearance. Roofs are normally pitched, with tile or slate finish. Floors may be of concrete, probably of the "filler-joist" type: any evidence of structural movement of these floors or long-standing dampness affecting them should be viewed with considerable caution. The structural adequacy of any balconies may be suspect. The larger blocks of Victorian mansion flats are often very impressive, with much architectural detail. Flats of this type in the central London area command very high prices.

Purpose-Built Blocks of Flats, Built in the Inter-War Period. This group of flats includes those in the style of the modern movement in architecture, dating from the 1930s, with concrete, or at least cement-rendered walls, painted white, steel window-frames and flat roofs. White-painted rendering does not weather well in our climate. Roof parapets are often a problem, chimney stacks may suffer from sulphate attack, and the early steel casements are likely to have rusted. Drainage faults are not uncommon. Planning and fittings often fall short of modern standards.

Flats, up to Four Storeys in Height, Built Post-1945. It is only in this period that it has become common for flats to be sold freehold or let by way of long lease, and virtually all the flats constructed by private developers have been built for sale. Whereas, prior to this period, flat developers were limited to London and a very few other larger centres of population, they are now found in many towns throughout the country.

The majority of these newer flat developments are limited to three storeys in height, or occasionally four, and are built in load-bearing brick construction with concrete unit floors, and do not incorporate lifts. The most serious structural defects affecting newer blocks of flats are usually settlement problems. Dampness due to detailing faults is not uncommon.

Multi-storey Flats Built Post-1945. Flats above four storeys in height are in a different league in so far that they normally require a framed structure and lifts are essential. High blocks need careful detailing, especially of windows, to counteract possible high-wind-pressures. Maintenance of multi-storey blocks can pose severe problems. Routine cleaning and maintenance can usually be done from a cradle, provided there is one. However, dealing with major repairs, such as spalling brickwork panels or exposure of concrete re-inforcement, is likely to require scaffolding, at considerable expense. If major structural repairs are needed, or likely to be needed in the forseeable future, the high cost of these is likely to be reflected in the service charges levied on flat-owners and thus could have a very marked effect on the value of flats in the block. This, coupled with the necessary very complex service installations, make the survey of a flat in a multi-storey block, which may be in excess of 20 storeys in height, a very demanding exercise indeed.

Multi-Storey System-Built Flats. Where a multi-storey block is "system-built" using pre-cast concrete units, the potential problems are even more complex, and any building society valuer called upon to survey a flat in a block of this type would do well to call for a report on the structure from a firm of chartered structural engineers with experience of this type of construction.

Building Society Policy. Before carrying out the survey of a flat for a building society, the valuer is advised to check that the flat in question comes within the scope of the current lending policy of the particular society. Valuers should not receive instructions to survey properties which are outside this policy but occasionally some get through. There is no doubt that flats do not provide as good security for mortgage advance as houses. Whilst they are now widely accepted and most societies will lend on flats, some societies exclude certain types of flats from their lending policy.

8.2. High Alumina Cement Concrete

In June, 1973, the roof at a school in Camden collapsed. This was followed by the collapse of a similar roof at a school in Stepney in February, 1974. The cause was attributed to the deterioration or "conversion" of pre-cast concrete members manufactured from high alumina cement concrete. Near panic ensued and official reports stated that all buildings incorporating high alumina cement concrete must be considered suspect. These buildings were to be identified and tests made to confirm whether or not the concrete was in order. There are something like 20 million square metres of floors and flat roofs constructed in HACC pre-cast units in perhaps as many as 50 thousand buildings. Building society opinion, expressed through the Building Societies Association Panel of Surveyors, whilst adopting a cautious attitude, pointed out that there had been no known cases of collapse of floors due to the use of HACC.

High alumina cement has two attractive characteristics: firstly that it produces concrete which is resistant to chemical attack; secondly that it develops strength very quickly. This latter characteristic was put to good use in the manufacture of pre-stressed, pre-tensioned, pre-cast concrete members suitable for floors and roofs as it enabled manufacturers to achieve a daily production cycle, since it was possible to stress the concrete at the age of about 18 hours. If ordinary Portland cement was used, the plant was only able to operate on a four or five day cycle and on this basis it was found more economic to use the much more expensive high alumina cement. Production of units of this type using HACC commenced about 1950 and became widespread thereafter.

It was always understood that HACC could be subject to the process known as conversion, however it was thought that this occurred only in warm and moist conditions and it was presumed that in the ordinary use in a domestic or commercial building such conditions of high temperature and humidity would not occur, or would not be of such a duration as to cause conversion.

The outcome was that very few buildings were found to be unsafe and that in respect of residential property, sub-committee T of the Building Regulations Advisory Committee on HACC issued the following advice:

"Wholly residential property of less than 5 storeys containing HACC is exempt from examination by a qualified consulting engineer and properties conforming with the following conditions may be deemed to be safe.

(a) The buildings do not consist of more than four storeys.

(b) In the case of roofs of HACC construction (1) they are of joist and block or composite construction, (2) they are not used for access, except for maintenance, (3) the spans do not exceed 6·5 m clear (21'4") in the case of standard I joists having a depth of 7" or less (×7) and 8·5 m clear (27'10") in the case of similar beams having depths of 9" or 10") (×9 and ×10).

(c) There is no persistent leakage or sustained heavy condensation.

Buildings which do not comply with these conditions should have the HACC examined by a suitably qualified consulting engineer and if it receives his approval may also be regarded as in safe structural condition."

The Building Societies Association advised their members that when asked for a loan on "exempt" property a society should lend as usual unless the valuer specifically advised against it because of deterioration in the HACC (or, of course, because there was some other defect not related to HACC). As regards "non-exempt" buildings, the B.S.A. Council expressed the view to members that they should entertain applications for advances on them but that they should withhold offers of advance until the properties had been appraised by a qualified engineer.

When carrying out surveys on properties built or altered between 1950 and 1974 and containing pre-cast concrete elements, the valuer should make sure that the building satisfies the criteria for exemption. If in doubt, or if the building does not satisfy the requirements for exemption, the surveyor should request the vendor or his agent to provide evidence that the building does not contain high alumina cement, or that if it does a structural engineer has inspected it and found it to be satisfactory.

Even in exempt buildings the valuer should be on the

look-out for evidence of water leakage as HACC which is in a converted state will virtually disintegrate over a period of about 3 years if there is persistent water leaching through alkalis from ordinary Portland cement, *e.g.* from screeds or through sulphates such as are sometimes present in plaster.

8.3. Fire Precautions in Flats

The construction of flats is controlled by the Building Regulations which lay down standards of fire-resistance for certain elements of structure, provisions for protected shafts (including enclosed stairways) and control of surface finishes. Means of escape are controlled by the Building Standards (Scotland) Regulations 1963 and the London Building Acts operative in the Inner London Boroughs but in the rest of England and Wales they did not come under the control of the Building Regulations prior to the 1976 revision.

Section 3 of the Fire Precautions Act 1971 gives power to Fire Authorities to require that a Fire Certificate shall be obtained for premises which have been or are being used as a dwelling in cases where there is living accommodation:

(1) Below the ground floor of the building; or
(2) Two or more floors above the ground floor of the building; or
(3) Of which the floor is 6 m or more above the surface of the ground on any side of the building.

The section does not apply to

(a) any premises consisting of or comprised in a house which is occupied as a single private dwelling; or
(b) any premises consisting of or comprised in a house which is occupied by persons who do not form a single household.

Where the Fire Authority give notice that a Fire Certificate is required, they must, on application for that Certificate, make an inspection of the building with particular reference to:

(a) Means of escape in case of fire with which the premises are provided; and
(b) the means (other than means for fighting fire) with which the relevant building is provided for securing that the means of escape with which the premises are provided can be safely and effectively used at all material times; and

(c) the means for fighting fire (whether in the premises or affecting the means of escape) with which the relevant building is provided for use in case of fire by persons in the building; and

(d) the means with which the relevant building is provided for giving the persons in the premises warning in case of fire.

If the Fire Authority are satisfied that these means are such as may reasonably be required in the circumstances of the case in connection with the use of the premises they must issue a Fire Certificate covering that use. If, however, the Authority is not satisfied that the means listed above are such as may reasonably be required in the circumstances of the case they must serve a notice specifying the steps which must be taken, by way of making alterations or otherwise, to satisfy the Authority.

Details of means of escape are given in British Standard Code of Practice CP 3 Chapter IV Part 1 1971 Precautions against Fire—Flats and Maisonettes (In Blocks over Two Storeys). This Code superseded CP 3 Chapter IV Part 1 1968 Fire Precautions in Flats and Maisonettes over 80 ft in height.

The Code of Practice is a fairly complicated document incorporating 26 pages of diagrams illustrating means of escape in different circumstances.

Most blocks of flats constructed since the publication of the above Codes of Practice do have adequate means of escape. However, there are exceptions and many older flats, especially conversions, fall short of the recommendations of the Codes. Fire alarm systems are not installed in many blocks of flats.

A valuer inspecting a flat in a block higher than two storeys must attempt to make some assessment of the costs of work which may be necessary to obtain a Fire Certificate, if the Fire Authority should exercise their rights under Section 3 of the Fire Precautions Act 1971. It is not an easy exercise to make such an assessment as the Act lays down subjective rather than objective standards—"such as may reasonably be required in the circumstances". It is suggested that a valuer might approach the problem by comparing the flats being inspected with the recommendations of the Code of Practice and then making an approximate estimate of the likely costs of the work in the whole block, assuming that the Fire Authority take a rigorous approach. The costs for the block can then be apportioned between the individual flats and the surveyor will then reflect the apportioned figure in either his valuation or recommended limit of advance, or both.

8.4. The Management of Flats

Besides making his physical inspection of the flat itself, the common parts and the main structure of the block, the valuer will need to make some investigations into the following matters, especially points 4 and 5, before he can complete his recommendation to the building society.

(1) The means of transfer
(2) The regulations governing the occupation of the flats
(3) The extent of the owner's obligations to repair
(4) The obligations of the lessor or management company in respect of structural repairs, maintenance of common parts and provision of services and the service charges payable by the lessee to cover these items.
(5) The type of management scheme
(6) The arrangements for insurance.

Most of the information on these points can be obtained from the draft conveyance or lease which should be available from the vendor's agent. These points are considered further below.

Means of Transfer. It is the solicitor's job to advise on this point but the valuer should be aware of the more usual arrangements. Flats involve the acceptance of many burdens and obligations for which leasehold tenure is more appropriate, especially for large schemes where there is a management company or lifts to be maintained or services provided. On the other hand for maisonettes and small schemes, the flat owner may be better off with a freehold.

Scotland has its own system, where a large proportion of property is held on feu. One point at which Scottish law differs from English is that some feuing conditions are enforceable by persons other than the superior, where, for example, a superior feus out lots of land on which buildings are to be erected but where one feuar may in certain circumstances object to another feuar breaching the feuing conditions.

Two-storey self-contained flats, each possessing their own separate entrance from ground-floor level, are relatively simple and can be dealt with by means of positive covenants from the owner of the ground-floor flat to provide support for the first floor and from the owner of the first-floor flat to maintain the roof. Provision needs to be made for the repair of party floors and shared services.

Positive covenants can be made enforceable by the granting of long leases coupled with the vesting of the freehold reversion in the other lessee; or by the lessor granting the lease of one of the units and then selling the freehold of the other subject to the lease; or by the lessor granting leases of each unit, in which case the purchasers look to the developer or his successors to carry out the lessor's obligation: this calls for ground rents to be sufficient to ensure that the lessor is a person of substance. Sometimes there is provision for the owners of the two units to enter into deeds of mutual covenant. Positive covenants to insure are also required. The front garden of two-storey units is sometimes conveyed with the lower flat and the back garden with the upper flat; or the owners can hold the gardens as tenants in common; or one owner can hold the gardens with the other having an easement to use them; or each can own half with the other having an easement over the half. Easements will be required for access to and repair or renewal of any water tanks in the roof and any joint service pipes or drains. The upper flat will need an easement to place scaffolding or ladders for repairs or window cleaning. The law will imply the grant or reservation of such easements as may be necessary to give effect to the common intention of the parties. Any valid easement imports all ancillary rights reasonably necessary to its use and enjoyment. For example, an easement of drainage carries with it the rights to repair the drain and to enter upon the servient tenement to do so and an easement of support carries the right to enter upon the servient land to carry out necessary repairs.

The owner of the upper flat enjoys an implied right of support and is entitled to enter the ground floor to take necessary steps to ensure that the support continues, by repairing those parts of the building which give support. The owner of the ground floor flat is not entitled to remove any support without providing an equivalent.

The main difficulty in the conveyance of flats freehold is that of making the burden of positive covenants run with the land. This can be overcome by means of a variable rent charge. In

"The Sale of Flats" (Sweet and Maxwell) George & George state, "When the flat owners all enter into covenants with the vendor and the other flat owners to contribute to the costs of the maintenance of common parts the situation appears indistinguishable from that in *Morland* v. *Cook* (1868) LR6 Eq. 252 and the obligations bind their successors in title. The person subject to such a rent charge cannot redeem it under the Law of Property Act 1925 Section 191 for that section clearly contemplates only rent charges of fixed amounts".

Alternatively the positive covenants can be made conditions of easements, or there can be a system of mutual deeds of covenant.

None of these arrangements can be effective unless the developer has covenanted to require every purchaser and lessee of the flats in a block to observe the restrictive covenants, to maintain the main structure and common parts and to insure the block.

The lease is a far more popular means for the sale of flats. It has the advantages that there is no difficulty over the right of re-entry. (Note that the Leasehold Reform Act does not apply to flats). Covenants will be in two groups, those with the lessor alone and those with the lessor and other lessees.

If the lessor disposes of such beneficial interest as he has, it is not possible for him to do so without also passing the burden of his obligations to his successor. Flat leases should contain arbitration clauses, as most disputes that are likely to arise can best be settled by a chartered surveyor or incorporated valuer.

Sale by way of underlease presents no difficulties.

The sale of flats by assignment of lease requires that leases are drawn for the purpose of assignment in parts. Otherwise the developer may disappear after he has sold his flats, leaving no one to look after the management of the block, and there is a danger of the head lease being forfeited.

Restrictive Covenants. A flat scheme needs to have regulations, made by way of restrictive covenants, for the mutual benefit of all the occupiers. Typical clauses include:

Not to use the flat except as a private dwelling for the occupation of one family;

Not to use the flat for any purpose which could cause a nuisance to the owners, lessee and occupiers of other flats in the development or in the neighbourhood;

Not to use the flat for any illegal purpose;

Not to throw rubbish or refuse into sanitary fittings, sinks, waste or soil pipes;

Not to play any musical instruments, record player, radio, etc., or to practice singing in the flat so as to cause annoyance to the owners, lessees or occupiers of the other flats in the development or so as to be audible outside the flat between the hours of 10 p.m. and 9 a.m.;

Not to do anything to render void or voidable the policy of insurance on any flat in the scheme or to cause the insurance premium payable to be increased;

Not to place any name, sign or advertisement on or in any window or on the exterior of the flat so as to be visible from the outside;

Not to hang any clothes or any other articles outside the flat;

Not to shake mats, dusters, etc., out of the windows of the flat;

Not to keep any dog or other animal or bird which may cause annoyance to any owner, lessee or occupier of other flats in the block;

Not to decorate the exterior of the flat other than in accordance with the colour scheme to be agreed by the majority of owners or lessees;

Not to erect any external wireless or television aerial;

Not to park on the site or in the garage any vehicle other than a private motor car or motor cycle.

Positive Covenants. Besides the covenant to observe the restrictions imposed as part of the flat scheme there will normally be positive covenants with the vendors and owners of the other flats to do the following:

To repair and maintain the flat itself.

To repair and maintain the main structure (or parts of it) and/or common parts and/or garden (normally in cases of two-storey flats only.)

To contribute towards the cost of maintenance and repair of the main structure, common parts, common services, gardens, etc.

To pay a rent charge or ground rent.

To contribute a due share of the water rate (where there is only one common main and the block is rated as a whole).

To register transfers or conveyance with the rent-charge owner or lessor.

Service Charges. The person responsible for the main structure and common parts expects to be fully reimbursed by the flat owners and his obligations are conditional upon his being reimbursed. The importance of this item can be appreciated by the fact that service charges in excess of £1,000 p.a. (exclusive of heating) are now quite common, for example on the South Coast.

The transfer or lease will set out details of the service charge. These are likely to include:

Covenants by the developer to repair and maintain;

A schedule of the expenses which the services charge is to include;

A covenant by the flat owners to pay contributions in accordance with a formula;

Provisions for provisional assessments and pre-payments;

Provision for a sinking fund for the replacement of major items;

Provisions for keeping and presentation of proper accounts;

Provision for the resolution of disputes, preferably by arbitration by a chartered surveyor or incorporated valuer to be appointed, in the event of failure to agree on a name, by the president for the time being of the Chartered Institute of Arbitrators.

A provision that the developer can only sell the rent charges if he appoints the transferree as trustee in his place will prevent the developer selling his rent charges and then disappearing.

Repairs. The split of responsibility for repairs is very much the concern of the valuer as it may affect the value of the flat. It is usual for the owner/occupier/lessee to be responsible for all the repairs and maintenance actually within his flat but not for the main structure. The definition of the extent of the flat so far as this is relevant to the questions of repair is important and in particular in the following areas:

(a) Walls and partitions. Is the lessee responsible for the upkeep of the interior faces of external or separating walls only, or in the case of dividing walls between flats does liability extend to the centre line of such partitions?

(b) Windows, including frames, sashes, casements and glazing. In the absence of any specific definition the lessee is likely to be responsible for windows inserted into openings in external walls and complete in themselves but not for windows which form part of a wall, e.g. in the case of a curtain wall.

(c) Entrance doors.

(d) Ceilings and floors. The liability for ceilings may extend merely to the decorative surface or more likely will include ceiling plaster, or plasterboard, and fixings. Liability for floors may extend to the floor boards only, or include responsibility for the joists and sub-structure below. Concrete floors are often classed as part of the main structure.

(e) Service connections. Who is responsible for electrical cables, water pipes, soil pipes, ventilation ducts, television aerial cables, telephone cables and entry-phone cables running to or from the flat?

The valuer should particularly be on the lookout for onerous responsibilities such as the obligation for the owner of the top flat to maintain the roof.

The lessor (or recipient of the service charge) is normally responsible for the following:

(a) Repair and maintenance of the main structure. It is desirable that this responsibility should extend to include "structural defects", otherwise repairing obligations under the lease may not extend to such defects.

(b) Repair and maintenance of common parts. It is useful if the standards of lighting and cleaning are specified rather than left vague.

(c) Repair and maintenance of common services, rainwater pipes and drains.

(d) Repair and servicing of lifts.

(e) Cleaning and maintenance of refuse chutes.

(f) External painting. It is helpful if the standard and frequency are referred to rather than left vague.

(g) Maintenance and upkeep of drives, forecourts, gardens and boundary walls.

(h) In some cases hot water and central heating are provided from a central boiler plant.

(i) Occasionally there are provisions for the employment of a caretaker.

There cannot be rights *in rem* to such services as the

provision of hot water and central heating. Thus in the case of a flat granted in fee simple failure cannot be remedied by specific performance and so in these circumstances the normal arrangement is that of a long lease. A lease is also preferable where there is a lift.

Costs of Repairs and Services. The valuer will easily ascertain the current service charge payable. Having done so he will need to attempt to gauge whether it is likely to be adequate to cover the outstanding and anticipated work. The danger signals are an obvious back-log of maintenance coupled with a minimal service charge, in which case steep increases in the service charge may be anticipated, or the continuing deterioration of the situation due to an ineffective management arrangement. In either case the security offered by the flat is likely to be affected.

Where the valuer meets a case where a major repair, such as complete reroofing, is necessary, his enquiries may indicate that a sinking fund has been built up to meet the costs of such repair. If this is not the case the probability of an increased burden on the flat owners should be reflected in his valuation of the flat.

Where repairs are necessary which are the responsibility of the lessor or management company rather than the individual lessee, there is little that the building society valuer can do other than require the applicant to give an undertaking that the need for these repairs to be done is drawn to the attention of those who are responsible for them. It is no good suggesting retentions or asking for under-takings for work to be carried out when the responsibility does not rest with the borrower. If the repairs are particularly serious and it is clear that the management company is not on top of its task, the valuer has the following options:

(a) To devalue the flat.
(b) To limit the percentage advance.
(c) To recommend against an advance being made.

Example

Check the adequacy of a service charge at £100 p.a. for a flat in a three storey block of 12 flats. The lease indicates that the charge covers repairs to main fabric, including external doors and windows, external painting, cleaning and maintenance of

common parts and grounds, insurance and fees of managing
agents.

	£
Assessment of annual costs of repairs to roof, gutters and downpipes, walls (pointing), external windows, staircases, service connections, drains, etc.	500
External painting and decoration of common parts; assume redecoration every 3 years: ⅓ of estimated cost of £600	200
Maintenance of grounds including part-time gardener, equipment and materials Cleaning of common parts including part-time cleaner, and materials	800
Lighting of common parts (and rates payable on any service outbuildings)	50
Insurance of flats and common parts	350
Management charges	500
Estimated total annual service charges for block	£2,400
No. of flats	12
Estimated annual service charge per flat	£ 200

Therefore the current charge of £100 p.a. is low and will have
to be increased or maintenance, etc, with fall short of an
acceptable standard. In view of this a reduction in the recommended percentage advance may be appropriate.

Management Arrangements. The management of a block of
flats may be handled in several ways, including the following:
    (1) By the developer retaining an interest.
    (2) By the freehold being vested in a management company
consisting of the flat owners. This is generally considered to be
the best method for a new block of flats. The company may be
limited or unlimited, with or without share capital or a society
formed under the Industrial and Provident Societies Act 1965.
A Board of Management is usually appointed by the members
from among their number and the Board in turn usually
appoints a chartered surveyor or incorporated valuer to look
after the management of the flats.

(3) In the cases of freehold flats rent-charges may be transferred to a management company consisting of all the flat owners.

(4) By managing agents with a concurrent lease. When the developer has granted head leases to all the flat purchasers he grants a concurrent lease to managing agents, vesting in them the benefits and burdens of the flat leases.

(5) By a lease granted to an interposed management company. This is likely to be unsatisfactory as with no profit rental, the management company is likely to have difficulty funding day to day repairs and will be unlikely to be able to pay if a lessee claims damages against it on the grounds of its failure to do the repairs. This lack of assets may make it impossible for the company to take proceedings against a flat owner who avoids his obligation to join the company or does not pay his service charge. For these reasons the building societies' solicitor may well advise that the flat does not provide suitable security for advance, even though the valuer's report may have been favourable.

(6) By a collateral management company existing side by side with the lessor but with no estate in the land. This has similar drawbacks to the latter case plus the problem that the covenant to pay the service charge, whilst binding the original lessee will not bind subsequent assignees. In these circumstances the building societies' solicitor will almost certainly advise that the flat should not be taken into mortgage.

(7) By the establishment of a maintenance trust fund. This is another case of complete separation of the right to receive rent and the obligation to carry out maintenance. As with the latter two cases there is the problem of insufficency of assets. In the event of the trustee failing to carry out his obligations the only remedy for the flat owner is to commence an administration in the Chancery Division. This is another case where the building societies' solicitor will advise against the property being taken into mortgage.

Summary: A valuer visiting a block of flats will sometimes get an impression that all is not well. The tell-tale signs are common parts in a dirty state, accumulated maintenance and the obvious mis-use of one or more flats—all factors which point to a failure in the management of the block. The causes may be an inadequately drafted lease, a management company lacking sufficient funds, the class of tenants or just bad management. Whatever the cause, such conditions sound a note of caution to the valuer who will probably advise against a maximum advance, or perhaps even against any advance at all.

8.5. The Insurance of Flats

Flats may be insured either by the lessor alone under a block policy or by the individual lessees.

Block Policy. This has considerable advantages for the lessor in that all his liabilities are covered and only one premium is payable. From the lessees point of view however there are several disadvantages:

(a) In the event of the impracticability of re-building, the lessee may not get his share of the insurance monies.

(b) The lessee is unlikely to be covered in respect of any claims arising from damage to chattels in the flat below as a result of escape of water and for which he may be liable.

(c) The block policy may not cover the lessees liability to third parties in his flat.

(d) Payment of rent and for temporary accommodation whilst the flat is uninhabitable are not likely to be covered.

A prudent building society will therefore require the lessee to take out supplemental insurance to cover any of the above risks which are not adequately covered by the block policy, including insurance to cover the position if for any reason the block policy lapses. The lessee will also need to insure his own contents.

Separate Policies. Where flats are to be insured individually there are normally provisions for the lessor to stipulate:

(a) that the insurance must be placed with a company nominated by the lessor. This is important in order that all insurance is placed with one company and inter-company disputes are avoided. There will often be an arrangement whereby insurance must be placed through the lessor's agency.

(b) that the insurance must be in the joint names of the lessor and the lessee.

(c) the perils to be insured against.

(d) either a minimum sum in which the flat must be insured or a requirement that it be insured in the "full-reinstatement value".

(e) that the insurance monies will be used in re-building or reinstatement but that in the event of failure or inability to re-build or reinstate the money should be divided between the lessor and the lessee in proportion to their respective interests in the property.

Where there are separate policies it is important that provisions are made for the insurance of the common parts.

Two possible problem areas with flat insurance are:

(1) Settlement or subsidence. If a block of flats suffers from settlement or subsidence it is quite likely that the flats in the block will become unsaleable. Yet many insurance policies for flats do not provide cover against settlement or subsidence. Even where there is a 10 year N.H.B.C. agreement in force, there is still some need for insurance against subsidence or settlement, as there is some doubt as to whether the N.H.B.C. agreement extends to structural defects affecting the common parts which remain vested in the vendor.

In cases where the lessor or management company do not insure against settlement or subsidence, lessees and mortgagors should attempt to make provisions to cover against these risks by means of supplemental cover in order to safeguard their interests in the property.

(2) Under-insurance. This could be disastrous in the event of a total loss. It could also have serious consequences in respect of a partial loss in that flat policies, unlike house policies, are normally subject to average. Thus it is in everybody's interests, including those of the building society, that a block of flats is adequately insured.

The appropriate cover for two-storey flats can normally be calculated quite simply, using the B.C.I.S. Guide to House Building Costs for Insurance Valuation. The determination of the appropriate cover for blocks of three or more storeys is by no means easy and gets progressively more difficult as the number of storeys increases.

Rates per square foot for flats are given in Spons' "Architects' and Builders' Price Book," issued annually, but it is submitted that in this connexion it is totally unsafe to rely on these as there are so many variables, including:

age and type of construction;
location;
size and number of storeys;
floor/wall ratio;
quality of finishes and fittings;
extent of services, especially lifts.

The only way to arrive at a replacement cost that can be relied on is for approximate quantities to be prepared on an elemental basis in the same manner that B.C.I.S. have done for house rebuilding costs and as is standard practice amongst

those firms of surveyors that specialise in fire insurance valuations. If the society is going to check adequately that there is
proper cover it will need to know the total sum for which the
block is insured and the proportion of that sum which is
attributable to the flat being taken into mortgage. To provide
these figures with any degree of reliability is quite beyond the
scope of the normal building society valuation and what in fact
tends to happen is that the valuer puts an arbitrary rate per
square foot on the flat he is surveying, makes additions for a
proportion of the common parts, temporary propping and
clearance of debris, architect's and surveyor's fees and for
inflation where the property is not index-linked. It is submitted
that this can be misleading and dangerous and that if the
society were to suffer a loss because of under-insurance the
valuer might well be held to be negligent unless he had
previously agreed with the society that insurance valuations
for flats would be carried out on this unreliable and arbitrary
basis only.

Even if an appropriate rate per square foot is hit upon there
are additional potential problems, including:

(a) The planning authority and Building Regulations may
    require substantial alterations before they will permit
    rebuilding to take place, e.g. deeper foundations.
(b) Professional fees will be considerable, as it is likely that
    consulting structural engineers and consulting services
    engineers will have to be retained as well as architects
    and quantity surveyors.
(c) If the block is framed and the frame has been damaged to
    the extent that demolition is required, the costs of demoli-
    tion of, say, a reinforced concrete frame with *in situ* floors
    several storeys high, can be very substantial indeed.

In the writer's opinion the answer to this problem is for those
responsible for the management of blocks of flats to have
valuations for insurance professionally carried out and made
available to flat-owners and prospective purchasers. These
valuations could be professional up-dated say every five years
with interim adjustments being made by reference to published
indices. Such a professional valuation would be in the interests
of all concerned with a block of flats and it is suggested that
building society valuers might make it a condition of advance
that such a valuation is made available.

Chapter 9

New Property

9.1. Inspecting New Property

In order to advise the society properly in connection with property to be built, the valuer will need to know the tenure and proposed purchase price or cost of the new property and its site. In addition he will need to peruse a copy of the basic working drawings and brief specification. The type of plan on the usual estate agent's handout is not adequate—a plan to the standard required for a Building Regulation submission is needed. The existence of Planning Permission and Building Regulation approval should be confirmed, together with the availability of mains services and the builder's N.H.B.C. registration.

The site must be inspected, when the valuer will be looking out for any abnormal ground conditions, such as a pond or mineshaft, where the house is to be located! When ground is steeply sloping, or clearly of low bearing capacity, confirmation should be sought that the foundations are being designed and supervised by a qualified civil or structural engineer. An attempt should be made to assess how the house will fit on to the site when completed, and what sort of outlook there will be.

The perusal of the drawings should reveal any non-standard form of construction about which further information or assurances might have to be requested. The site plan should indicate if there are drainage problems, such as the necessity for a sewage pump. The adoption of sewers is discussed in Chapter **2.10.**

The liability for paving and sewer charges must be determined: if the new house is on an estate there will probably be road and sewer agreements with the Local Authority. These are discussed in Chapter **2.11.**

The valuation of a property to be built should be the value as at the date of inspection, making the assumption that the property is completed at that date. In fact, by the time the house is completed, the value may well have increased as a result of inflation, but it is common practice to let the original valuation figure stand on subsequent re-inspection reports during construction and on completion.

New properties will tend to fall into three categories.

(1) Houses or bungalows on new estates being built for sale by speculative builders or developers.
(2) Flats being built for sale in a development of several, or many, units.
(3) One-off houses or bungalows being built on a private basis by the prospective owner-occupier.

The valuation of the new property may be less than the purchase price, or on rare occasions, for example, where a builder is erecting a house for his own occupation, the valuation may be more than the cost or purchase price.

When large estates are being developed, the valuer has to consider if the size of the proposed development is such that it will exceed demand in the area. If this happens the estate may remain in an unfinished state for many years. Where a lot of units are completed but remain unsold, they may have a depressing effect on second sales on the estate, more especially if the builder drops his prices in order to move the completed houses and reduce his overdraft. If this happens, the security provided by mortgaged houses on the estate can be impaired.

9.2. Standards of Design and Construction

The standards to which most new houses will be built are those set out in the Registered House Builders' Handbook Part II: Technical Requirements for the Design and Construction of Dwellings, published by the National House Building Council. This is a first-class publication, incorporating a brief schedule of requirements, a schedule of facilities and services and a technical specification.

The requirements include, *inter alia*, the following:

Rq. 1—Building legislation.

Every dwelling shall comply with all relevant building legislation and the regulations of statutory undertakings and other proper authorities.

Rq. 2—Materials.

(a) All materials shall be suitable for the purpose for which they are used.
(b) The quality of any materials shall be not lower than that defined in the relevant British Standard.

(c) Where no British Standard is relevant, a traditional material shall be of the standard customary in the industry.

(d) All the materials shall be used strictly in accordance with the manufacturer's recommendation unless a higher standard is laid down in the specification.

(e) Proprietary materials which are to be used for critical functions in a dwelling shall have been satisfactorily assessed by an appropriate independent authority. Critical functions include structure, weather-proofing, thermal and sound insulation, services, fire resistance.

Rq. 3—Facilities and services.

These to be provided in accordance with a schedule provided, and installed in accordance with the "deemed-to-satisfy" specifications or alternative specifications giving a not lower quality.

Rq. 4—Structure and finish.

Structure and finish shall be in accordance with the deemed-to-satisfy specifications provided or alternative specifications giving a not lower quality.

Rq. 5—Structural design for special conditions.

(a) This requirement applies to special conditions which include the foundations and superstructure of every dwelling over three storeys in height; certain types of foundations and retaining walls; any superstructure element which is not based on specific design criteria and any dwelling not constructed in accordance with U.K. traditional practice. (e.g. steel or timber framed).

(b) Structural design shall be carried out by a chartered civil or structural engineer or other professional person whose qualifications are acceptable to the Council,

(c) the design shall comply with all relevant codes of practice,

(d) the design shall relate to the site location and condition,

(e) in all cases the builder shall require the designer to issue clear instructions to site personnel, and not permit departure from the design without the designer's written consent.

Rq. 6—Workmanship.

(a) All work shall be carried out in a sound, neat, durable and workmanlike manner to the satisfaction of the Council.

(b) Reasonable precautions shall be taken to protect fixed and

unfixed materials against any damage likely to affect the
finished quality of the dwelling.

(c) Before hand-over of the dwelling to the purchaser, care
shall be taken to ensure that all work has been completed
and access provided; services have been tested and are in
working order; sanitary fittings and glass are free from
damage and have been cleaned; splashes of mortar, paint
and the like have been removed; floors have been cleaned;
rubbish and débris have been removed from the dwelling
and the garden.

The schedule of facilities and services deals with the following matters:

Internal planning	—S.	1	Measurement of floor areas
	S.	2	Kitchen planning
	S.	3	Storage accommodation
	S.	4	Bedrooms
	S.	5	Wardrobe cupboards
	S.	6	Airing cupboards
Services	—S.	7	Sanitary fittings
	S.	8	Water services
	S.	9	Heating to main living room
	S.10		Central heating
	S.11		Gas service
	S.12		Electricity service
Insulation	—S.13		Sound insulation
	S.14		Thermal insulation of roofs
Access	—S.15		Access to lofts
	S.16		Doors
External facilities	—S.17		External access
	S.18		Area immediately surrounding the dwelling
	S.19		Garden area

The technical specification which follows is a first-class brief
specification covering new dwellings. Its standards are equally
applicable to extensions and alterations. The sections comprise
foundations, concrete superstructure, brickwork superstructure, carpentry, roof coverings, joinery, glazing, services, wall
and ceiling finishes, painting, garages, drainage, drives and
paths, retaining and boundary walls.

This publication is one which every building society valuer
should be conversant with, and it provides an excellent check

list for the detailed inspection of any part of a new house, for example:

Fo. 3(b) deals with hazardous foundation conditions including high water table, sulphate in the ground or ground water, peat, mine and mineral workings past and present, made ground, trees, ground of low bearing capacity, former buildings on the site, adjacent buildings and existing drains.

Fo. 19(c) gives minimum distances for foundation depths in the proximity of trees.

Fo. 37(a) calls for through ventilation of underfloor voids.

Co. 14(a) requires vapour barriers/checks on the warm side of the thermal insulant to concrete roofs to minimise the risk of condensation and to ensure adequate vapour resistance.

Br. 7 covers the general workmanship of the brickwork, Br. 8, the installation of damp-proof courses, and Br. 9, pointing.

Ca. 19 calls for falls on flat roofs to be not less than 1 in 60.

Ca. 37 requires trussed rafter roofs to comply with CP. 112: Part III "Code of Practice for Trussed Rafter Roofs for Dwellings".

Ca. 37(b) requires proprietary jointing systems used in trussed rafters to have been satisfactorily assessed by an appropriate independent authority.

Jo. 2 requires door frames, windows, surrounds to metal windows, external doors other than flush doors and external timber features other than fencing to be constructed of timber that is pre-treated against fungal decay.

Jo. 7 specifies the acceptable moisture content for various timber elements.

Gl. 6 calls for external glazing to be carried out before flooring and internal joinery are fixed unless provision is made for protecting timber from damp.

Gl. 10 requires rebates to be primed before glazing.

Wf. 9 covers wall and ceiling finishes and reads as follows:

(a) The quality of finish shall be such that it is suitable for the situation.
(b) Surfaces shall be reasonably plane and smooth.
(c) Reveals, soffits to openings, external angles and the like shall be reasonably plumb or level.
(d) Ceiling lines and corners shall be of a reasonably regular appearance.

Pa. 4 will not allow wood having a moisture content above 18% to be primed or painted.

Pa. 5 discusses preparation, knotting and priming; Pa. 6, site preparation and painting.

Dp. 3 requires drives or paths abutting an external wall of a dwelling to be not less than 150 mm below the level of the damp-proof course in the wall and the surface of the drive or path to slope away from the wall.

Rb. 2(e) requires the design of retaining walls to be carried out by a chartered civil or structural engineer.

The garden areas are dealt with in paragraphs S.18 and S.19, which include the following provisions:

S.18(a) Where water-logging may reasonably be expected, suitable precautions shall be taken to prevent it.
S.19(b) Sub-soil shall not be left on top of vegetable soil.
    (d) Vegetable soil distributed shall be re-instated or replaced.
    (e) Rubbish and débris should be removed.

At the back of the book are practice notes relating to root damage by trees—siting of dwellings and special precautions; timber-frame dwellings; suspended floor construction for dwellings on deep fill sites, and reducing noise from w.c.s in dwellings.

Another useful publication from the N.H.B.C. is "Registered House Builders' Foundations Manual—Preventing foundation failures in new dwellings".

9.3. Properties of Non-Standard Construction

Bruce Allsopp, architectural philosopher and historian, has written in his book "Towards a Humane Architecture" (Muller) that, "In one field alone, the building societies, is finance readily available on a small scale and even here the architectural thinking of the building societies is notoriously reactionary, hostile to innovation and outrageously prejudiced against old property no matter how architecturally valuable". What Allsopp does not appreciate, and he is not alone, is that the building society must not take undue risks with its investors' savings. There is no doubt that certain types of older property, some inner city properties threatened by comprehensive re-development, and properties incorporating certain new techniques and materials, constitute above-average risks, sometimes to the extent that the valuer will deem it necessary to advise the society against accepting them as security for mortgage.

Timber-frame Dwellings. Section Ca. 27 of the N.H.B.C. Technical Requirements refers to timber-frame dwellings and states that "the design of timber-frame dwellings shall be undertaken by a competent person and evidence of adequate design shall be submitted to the Council prior to commencement on site". This submission is to be made on form HB210 for each house-type on each estate. This form includes a very detailed certificate which must be completed by a consulting chartered civil or structural engineer with appropriate experience in timber engineering. Other professionally qualified persons may be considered for acceptance by N.H.B.C. if the person concerned has appropriate experience. Facilities are to be made available to N.H.B.C. inspectors to see off-site fabrication, and detailed design and assembly information is to be available to N.H.B.C. inspectors on request. A timber-frame dwelling is defined as one in which the outer walls are constructed of load-bearing timberwork instead of traditional brickwork or blockwork. Such studwork may be clad with a brick or block veneer. The practice note explains the reason for requiring the submission of form HP120 in the following terms, "Many builders and their workmen are now building timber-frame dwellings without previous experience of this form of construction. Because timber and timber-based sheet materials are imported into Britain, there is considerable emphasis here on economy in their use. Experience shows that careful calculation is essential to ensure that a dwelling is structurally adequate. Similarly, experience shows that it is necessary for all details to be thoroughly prepared at the design stage, and not be left to the man on the site to follow traditional practice; for him there is likely to be no relevant tradition. All this is in contrast to North America, Scandinavia and other countries, where timber-frame is the traditional method of building, and expertise has been built up over generations".

Thus with new timber-framed dwellings, the building society valuer will normally have the assurances that the dwellings have satisfied the requirements of both the Building Regulations and the N.H.B.C., including structural design by a qualified engineer. In these circumstances he should have no qualms about accepting the property as suitable security for mortgage, although the non-standard form of construction must be drawn to the attention of the society and may well affect the insurance premium. The situation is nothing like as straightforward in the case of second and subsequent sales, especially were the property concerned was erected before

January, 1974, when the present N.H.B.C. arrangement came into operation. The surveyor may be able to determine the manufacturer whose system was used and if it was a well-known firm of good standing the risk will be small. On the other hand if there is no information at all available, especially in the case of a two-storey building, the valuer may consider it best not to accept the property as security for mortgage unless an entirely satisfactory architect's or consulting engineer's report is first obtained.

A common fault in the detailing of timber-framed buildings is to fix the sole plate to the concrete slab by a method which punctures the damp-proof membrane.

External Claddings. Claddings other than stone, brick, certain types of concrete block and cement rendering, etc., should be treated with some caution. Timber cladding should be pre-treated against decay. Vertical tiling must have a moisture barrier behind it and have every tile nailed with two corrosion-resistant nails.

The N.H.B.C. Technical Handbook requires other claddings to have been satisfactorily assessed by an appropriate independent authority such as the Agrèment Board, the Building Research Establishment, Research Associations, etc.

Concrete Buildings. Section Co. 6 of the N.H.B.C. Handbook requires properties constructed in no-fines concrete to be designed by a chartered civil or structural engineer or other professional person whose qualifications are acceptable to the Council.

Section Co. 15 deals with pre-cast concrete system building and requires that

(a) materials and jointing techniques shall where appropriate have been satisfactorily assessed by an appropriate independent authority,

(b) structural design shall be caried out by a chartered civil or structural engineer or other professional person whose qualifications are acceptable to the Council.

Pre-cast concrete system building will normally be found in blocks of flats several storeys high. In view of doubts that have been expressed about the continuing structural stability of a small proportion of properties of this type of construction, it is recommended that the building society valuer should not recommend a property with this form of construction as suitable security for mortgage unless a comprehensive and entirely satisfactory consulting civil or structural engineer's report on the building is provided.

Concrete systems have also been used for single-storey housing and in this case the main danger is inadequate protection to the re-inforcement, resulting in rusting and the breaking down of the face of concrete panels or piers.

Steel-framed Houses. These are not common. The main danger is rusting of inadequately protected steelwork.

Other Non-Standard Forms. The valuer is likely to come across new materials and constructional techniques from time to time. Whenever he does he should adopt a cautious approach and ensure that he has proper assurances from suitably qualified sources.

9.4. Interim Valuations for Stage Payments

The valuation of a new property includes three elements.

(1) The value of the site.
(2) The costs of roads and sewers outside the curtilage of the site.
(3) The value of the building itself.

In order to make an interim valuation the surveyor must first split the total valuation on completion into these three elements.

In the case of a "one-off" house on an individual plot the value of the plot is determined by comparison with sales of similar plots. These will probably all be plots with roads and sewers already available and items 1 and 2 above are therefore grouped together as the composite cost of a serviced site.

On an estate, the cost of the site can be ascertained by dividing the average cost of similar building land per acre by the number of units per acre to be built on the estate. This will exclude roads and sewers and the figure to be included for these items should be the average figure for all the houses on the estate and not the costs for the actual road fronting the property in question. This average figure can be worked out by taking a typical house or by finding out from the developer the total cost of his road and sewer sub-contract and dividing this by the number of units on the estate.

The value of the building itself is the total final valuation figure less the value of the site and costs of roadworks. The interim valuation is the full market value on completion less the costs of completion of the building and roadworks; this is exactly the same figure as the value of the site plus costs of roadworks and building already carried out, *provided* that the value of the building itself does in fact fairly represent its construction cost. Where this is not the case and the valuer's calculations indicate that the costs of construction are in excess of the value of the building itself, then the interim valuation must be prepared by deducting the valuer's estimated costs of completion from the full market value on completion. This problem might occur where a house had extensive underbuilding but is being sold at the same price as similar houses on the same development which have no underbuilding: or in the case of an extensive "one-off" house perhaps being built by a small contractor who may have grossly under-estimated the cost of the work, or being built at an artificially low figure by a builder for his own occupation.

The interim valuation can include the full value of the site. A proportion of the costs of the road and sewer works can also be included, dependant upon how much of these works has been carried out. Time does not permit detailed calculations on each occasion and it is therefore necessary for the surveyor to devise some rule of thumb to give a quick assessment of the proportion of the road and sewer costs to be included. The following percentages provide such a guide.

	%
Excavation of hardcore to carriageway	18
Sewers and drainage	25
Kerbs and channels	11
Tarmac base course	12
Tarmac wearing course	8
Pavements	20
Lighting	6
	100

The total value attributable to the house can similarly be broken down in an approximate manner as follows in order to make a rough assessment of the value of the work completed. Again it must be stressed that average figures of this type can never provide a truly accurate value and judgment must be exercised by the valuer as appropriate.

	%
Substructure	8·3
External walls	14·7
Roof	7·0
Windows and external doors	13·0
Stairs	0·9
Upper floors	3·5
Internal walls and partitions	3·3
Internal doors	3·0
Plastering to walls	3·8
Ceilings	1·9
P.V.C. finish to ground floor	2·2
Decorations	3·0
Water installation	3·8
Central heating	7·0
Electrical installation	2·3
Gas installation	0·3
Fittings	1·6
Sanitary appliances	2·9
Site works	4·9
Drains	2·6
Garage	10·0
	100·0

Example

A freehold house and garage under construction on a new estate have just been roofed and glazed. Drains have been laid and roads hardcored. Prepare an interim valuation.

	£	£
Purchase price/valuation on completion		24,000
Value of site	3,000	
Average cost of road/sewer works for all houses on the estate	1,000	
		4,000
Proportion of total value attributable to house		20,000

At this stage the valuer should check that the proportion of the total value attributable to the building (i.e. in this case £20,000) fairly represents the estimated construction cost of the building. If this is the case the interim valuation may then be prepared as follows:-

Interim Valuation	%	£
Site at full value		3,000
Roadworks		
Excavation and hardcore	18%	
Drainage (partial) say	23%	
	——	
	41%	
	× £1,000	
	———	410
House	%	
Substructure	8·3	
External walls	14·7	
Roof,	7·0	
Windows and external doors	13·0	
Stairs	0·9	
Upper floors	3·5	
Garage	10·0	
Drains	2·6	
	——	
	60·0%	
	× £20,000	12,000
Total interim valuation		15,410

If roadworks are not included in the purchase price or if the road frontage to the property being valued is in excess of the average road frontage on the estate and there is no Road Agreement with the Local Authority, it will be necessary to adjust the above valuation accordingly.

As well as making an interim valuation, the valuer will inspect work carried out to check that it conforms with previously approved plans and that the materials and workmanship appear to be of an adequate standard. Any defective work should be reported to the building society and excluded from the interim valuation.

It is not appropriate for interim stage payments to be made on

flats, as a partially completed flat in a partially completed block
does not provide adequate security.

9.5. Guarantees

The one event which really gave teeth to the National House
Builders' Registration Council was the decision by the building
societies that mortgages would only be granted on new houses
built by registered house builders. There is no doubt that the
N.H.B.C. guarantee is very worthwhile, and many purchasers
have benefited substantially as a result of it.

Thus when considering a mortgage application on a new
house the valuer will need to know the name of the builder and
to confirm that he is N.H.B.C. registered, so that the society
may be advised accordingly. The easiest way of checking a
builder's registration is usually to ask him to provide documentary evidence of this. Alternatively enquiries may be made from
the N.H.B.C. or by reference to a current register.

If on a subsequent interim or final inspection of the new
house it becomes apparent that the builder has changed or if it
comes to the valuer's notice that the builder's registration
has lapsed, or he has been struck off the register or has gone
into liquidation, the valuer should advise the society accordingly in his report so that the solicitor can be made aware of the
problem. The responsibility for actually getting the N.H.B.C.
certificate rests with the solicitor, and it is apparently not
unusual for completion to take place before the actual certificate is to hand. This is an unfortunate practice which can lead
to difficulties if the builder subsequently goes into liquidation
before defects are made good.

Not all new houses are built by N.H.B.C. registered builders;
indeed some of the best new houses are not. This generally
occurs when a house is being built by a private individual for
his own occupation. The builder may be a traditional contractor whose normal work does not involve speculative house
building, or a small contractor who is not of sufficient substance to register, or the new house may be being built on a
trade by trade contract basis, or the applicant may be building
his own house. The writer's uncle, a teacher of building
construction, built his own ashlar stone house over a period of
five years, including quarrying and dressing his own stone. For
these cases the building societies will grant mortgages
provided construction has been supervised by an architect,

chartered surveyor or licentiate of the Institute of Builders, providing they are directly responsible to the building owner.

An architect means someone who is registered under the Architect's Registration Act 1938 and it is illegal for anyone not so registered to use the term architect (other than a landscape architect or naval architect). Corporate membership of the R.I.B.A. is adequate proof of registration, otherwise it is a matter of checking in the annual register published by the Architect's Registration Council. Caution is needed here as there are a number of firms who do architectural work but who are not registered architects and such designations as "architectural consultants" or "design group", etc., should raise suspicions. "Supervision" is not expected to include examination of every part of the works. It will only involve periodic visits but ought to examine all items of prime importance, in particular the foundations. In these cases a recommendation for mortgage advance should be conditional upon a statement being provided by an appropriate person stating that he has supervised the construction and that the work has been carried out satisfactorily. This wording is important, as otherwise the Society will have no assurance that construction has been supervised. The purpose of requiring this supervision is to safeguard both the applicant and the society and as the applicant will be paying a fee to his architect it is important to him that he should have a written assurance that the work is satisfactory.

From time to time a valuer will come across a new house which is not built by an N.H.B.C. registered builder and has not been supervised by an appropriate person. In these circumstances the society should be advised accordingly and an advance should not be recommended. This recommendation should be adhered to even when an architect has inspected the property on completion and provided a satisfactory report, as it is virtually impossible for him to certify that foundations are satisfactory in cases where these have not been inspected during construction.

Any defects are likely to manifest themselves after a period of time and it is becoming general practice to accept such properties as suitable security for mortgage after three years.

9.6. Final Inspections

On the final inspection of a new property the valuer will need to check that it has been built in conformity with the previously approved plans, that it has in fact been completed and that the materials and workmanship are of an adequate standard.

Where work is not completed, as is quite often the case, the valuer has to decide whether to advise the society that the advance should not yet be made, or that it should be made subject to a retention until certain specified outstanding works are completed, or that it should be made subject to the applicants giving an undertaking that they will ensure that certain specified outstanding items of work are completed within an appropriate time.

Occasionally a valuer will come across properties where the workmanship is of an unacceptably low standard. Where this occurs the surveyor must have the courage to say so and recommend accordingly. It is only if this is done that the worst types of house-building can be stamped out, but it should be appreciated that the agggrieved builder is likely to threaten reference to the valuer's professional institution, as a coercive exercise, or to make representations direct to the head office of the building society concerned!

Chapter 10

Further Inspections

10.1. Revaluations

Re-advance or larger advance. Where a borrower wishes to take a re-advance or larger advance, but is not proposing to carry out any extensions or improvements, all that is needed is an up-to-date valuation of the property and a current recommendation as to the security which it provides.

The valuer will be looking out for any factors which have changed since the original valuation. For example, especially if the house was bought as a brand-new property, it could be that differential settlement has subsequently occurred.

The valuer will also take note of the condition in which the property is being maintained. If routine maintenance has been totally disregarded it is probably unwise to recommend a further advance.

Where maintenance is reasonable, but some repairs are needed, a further advance can be recommended conditional upon the necessary repairs being done.

Where alterations to the description of the property have occurred since the previous inspection, details should be noted. These might include extensions, installation of fittings, etc.

Further advance for extensions, improvements or repairs. In this case the surveyor will have to assess the value of the property on completion of the extensions, improvements or repairs and to recommend an appropriate percentage advance on the increased valuation figure, together with an increased figure for insurance. The Society will then normally grant a further advance up to the recommended percentage, subject to satisfactory completion of the work but normally subject to the further advance not exceeding 80% of the costs of the works.

There are many occasions when the increase in value of the property will be less than the expenditure on the improvements. Occasionally the value of the property may increase by a sum in excess of the cost of the works. This will depend on the nature of the works to be carried out and how economically they can be done.

In order to advise in connection with extensions, improvements and repairs, the valuer needs to have copies of the proposed plans and/or specifications, estimates of cost and copies of statutory approvals where these are necessary.

Where statutory approvals are necessary but have not been obtained, any recommendation for further advance should be subject to these approvals being obtained.

Extensions and alterations are not subject to any N.H.B.C. guarantees. Therefore if the work is in any degree complex or extensive, or if the valuer feels a lack of confidence in the capabilities of the proposed builder, he should recommend that the further advance should be conditional on the works being supervised by a registered architect or chartered building surveyor, in which case the professional fees can be added to the estimates in computing the further advance.

On occasions, some societies have specifically asked their valuers to advise if the foundations shown on the drawings for extensions are adequate. In these circumstances all that the valuer can do is advise that the foundations are adequate in size and type (assuming they are) provided they are taken down to ground of adequate bearing capacity. The valuer is unlikely to be able to check this, as it would mean a visit at precisely the time the excavations have been completed but before the concrete is poured. However, the societies do have the safeguard that foundations are inspected by the Local Authority Building Inspector.

Where the valuer notices any obvious errors or inadequacies in the drawings or specification, these should be drawn to the attention of the society.

If the valuer forms the opinion that the estimate grossly overcharges for the work envisaged, he will do the borrower a service by recommending that it should be a condition of mortgage advance that alternative estimates are obtained.

Some societies endorse their offers of further advances to the effect that the offer does not give an implied warranty that the contractor's estimate represents the fair value of the work to be carried out.

Where an improvement grant is being obtained, the amount of this should be deducted from the vacant possession value on completion and the recommended percentage mortgage advance calculated on the balance (see Chapter 5).

Sometimes the valuer will form the opinion that the proposed works, rather than adding to the amenity of the property, will detract from it. Instances of this might be where a particularly badly designed and poorly constructed extension is proposed to a substantial house of character, or where cavity fill insulation is proposed to a property in an extremely exposed location. Another so-called "improvement" which should be actively discouraged and considered unsuitable for mortgage advance is the fixing of thin artificial stone facings to good brick terraced houses: not only is this finish quite out of character, but the pieces are usually stuck on without any respect for traditional masonry practice and no doubt they will start to fall off after a few years. Where proposed extensions and alterations are quite out of character with the existing building so far as proposed materials, proportions of windows, disposition of glazing bars, etc., are concerned, the valuer should recommend that the borrowers consult an architect and present a revised scheme. This is particularly important in areas where there are dominant local materials, and when extending and altering buildings which express the local vernacular tradition. On larger extensions these points will be taken up by the Planning Authority, but smaller extensions and alterations do not need specific planning approval. In these cases the building society valuer can exercise a very useful influence in the interests of environmental improvement, whilst at the same time helping the borrower to achieve a result likely to enhance his property.

Purchase of Additional Land. Occasionally the borrower has the opportunity to enlarge the site of his property by acquiring some adjacent land. As with extensions, the valuer must make a valuation of the property on completion of the purchase of the land and advise an appropriate percentage advance on this valuation.

The increase in the value of the property as a result of the purchase of the land may be less than the sum paid for the land, or it may be more. The amount of the advance will be calculated in a similar manner as for extensions, discussed above.

The valuer must satisfy himself that the land which is being acquired does not have any onerous liabilities attached to it, e.g., underground culverts, high retaining walls or liability for road charges. If there is a liability for road charges, these should be an appropriate retention.

To be suitable for a further advance, the interest in the land being purchased must be either freehold or long leasehold.

Purchase of Freehold. The Leasehold Reform Act 1967 empowers certain tenants to enfranchise or to extend their leases beyond the original term. Before a tenant can exercise these rights he must satisfy the following main conditions:

(1) His lease must be of a house which he occupies as his main residence. The Act does not apply to flats.

(2) He must hold a long lease, *i.e.*, a lease originally granted for more than 21 years.

(3) He must hold at a low rent, *i.e.*, at a rent which is less than $\frac{2}{3}$ of the rateable value on 23rd March 1965 or the initial assessment if first rated after that date.

(4) The rateable value at the times mentioned in (3) above must not exceed £400 in greater London or £200 elsewhere. These figures were increased by Section 118(1) of the Housing Act 1974 to £1,500 in Greater London and £750 elsewhere.

(5) He must have been in occupation for the five years, or five of the ten years, immediately before the time he seeks to exercise his rights under the Act.

Where a tenant satisfies these conditions he can require the landlord either to grant him an extension of his present lease for a period of 50 years or to sell him the unencumbered freehold interest. Where the occupier is a sub-lessee, he can nonetheless enfranchise or extend his lease against all superior interests to obtain the freehold interest in possession.

It is usually in the interests of lessees to obtain the freehold of their property and building societies will normally wish to encourage their members to do so by making further advances available toward the costs of acquiring the freehold, including the necessary legal and surveyor's fees. The alternative right of extending the lease for a period of 50 years is very much second-best especially as, where a tenant extends his lease under the Act, the landlord may nonetheless resume possession either at the end of the period of the original lease or at any time during the extension period where he can show that he intends to re-develop the property and this involves the demolition or substantial re-construction of the premises. It is therefore assumed that building society valuers will not normally be involved with extensions of the lease and these are not considered further.

The landlord who owned his interest before 18th February, 1966, can prevent both extension and enfranchisement if he can show that he reasonably requires the property at the end of the period of the original lease for occupation either by himself or another member of his family for their only or main residence, in which case compensation will be payable to the tenant.

The tenant cannot buy the freehold once the original term date has passed.

Enfranchisement is in effect the right of the tenant to acquire compulsorily the landlord's interest. As with compulsory purchase, valuation rules are set out in the Act for the determination of the price to be paid. These provide that the price shall be the open market value of the freehold interest, subject only to the tenancy, on the assumption that the tenant has no right to acquire the freehold interest but has exercised his right to extend the lease for 50 years. Properties with rateable values in the range £1,000–£1,500 in Greater London and £500–£750 elsewhere are valued on a different basis as set out in the Housing Act 1974, but the minister announced in November, 1978, that the Government intended to repeal Section 118(4) of this act and make provisions for all enfranchised houses to be valued on the same basis.

In outline the valuation approach is to value the rent for the unexpired term of the original lease, reverting to the modern ground rent for the 50 years of the extended lease (subject to rent review in the 25th year of this period), and reverting thereafter to the full freehold value in possession. Where the original lease plus the extension gives an unexpired term of over 65 years then the modern ground rent may be regarded as continuing in perpetuity.

Example

The borrower holds the tenancy of a house for the residue of a 99 year lease, amounting to 25 years, at an annual ground rent of £5·00. The rateable value is £85 and the borrower has occupied the property as his main residence for the last five years. Sites for the erection of equivalent modern houses are letting on building leases for 99 years at a rent of £20·00 per annum plus a premium of £1,500 per unit.

	£
Modern ground rent.	
Premium	1,500
Annual equivalent at 10%	× 0·1
	150 p.a.
Add rent paid	20
	£170 p.a.

Enfranchisement price	£	£
Term		
Ground rent receivable	5.00 p.a.	
Y.P. 25 years at 7%	11·65	
		58
Reversion to 50 years extension		
Modern ground rent	170 p.a.	
Y.P. in perp. def. 25 years at 10%	0.92	
		156
Enfranchisement price		214

Example.

The borrower holds the tenancy of a house for the residue of a 999 year lease granted in 1970 with an annual ground rent of £40·00. The rateable value is £180 and the borrower has occupied the house since 1970. Sites for the erection of similar houses in the area are selling at £5,000 per unit.

Enfranchisement price	£
Rent receivable	40·00
Y.P. in perp. at 10%	10·00
Enfranchisement price	£400·00

Because of the length of lease the ground rent is valued in perpetuity and the modern ground rent is not relevant.

As with the case of further advances for extensions or purchase of land, the valuer must value the property on completion of enfranchisement and the computation of the amount of the further advance will be on a similar basis as for cases of extensions, as discussed above.

A complication will arise in respect of enfranchisement where a site has development value. In such cases it is probable that the freeholder, on termination of the original lease-term, would prevent an extension of the lease under Section 17, subject to payment of compensation. The enfranchisement price assumes that the tenant has exercised his right to extend the lease but is also subject to the right of the landlord to prevent extension at the end of the original term. In these cases the enfranchisement price reflects the value of this power of the freeholder. In outline the valuation is the value of the rent from the original lease, then reversion to freehold in possession less the compensation payable to obtain possession. The basis of assessment of the compensation figure is basically the value of the tenant's right to extend his lease for 50 years, which he is being deprived from exercising: it will be assumed that the tenant will be limited to using the premises for the purposes to which they have been put since the commencement of the old lease and in most cases the compensation will be the capital value of the profit rent represented by the difference between the rental value as a dwelling house and the modern ground rent.

Transfer of Half of Equity. In many cases mortgages are granted jointly to husband and wife. With the sad trend of increasing separations and divorces, valuers will find themselves involved in re-valuations required in connection with the transfer of one half of the equity from one of the former partners in the marriage to the other.

This is a straightforward case of an up-to-date valuation taking into account any changes that have occurred since the original valuation. It is an observable fact that in cases where there has been matrimonial disharmony, routine maintenance is often found to have been neglected. Where repairs are found to be necessary, they should be drawn to the attention of the society.

10.2. Re-inspections

Inspection of Repairs. Where a mortgage has been recommended subject to a retention until certain repairs are carried out, the valuer will normally be asked to make a re-inspection when the repairs have been dealt with. Of all the cases which a building society valuer will handle this is normally the simplest and easiest, and these re-inspections can provide, in suitable circumstances, an opportunity for a trainee valuer to undertake an inspection on his own.

Sometimes it will be found that the repairs have not been done, or have only partially been done, or have not been done satisfactorily, in which case the society must be informed accordingly, with the recommendation that the retention should not be released, or at least only partially released.

Stage Payments for Extensions. These re-inspections will only occur in the case of large extensions, where the borrower has to make interim payments to his builder. Applications for interim advances should be backed up by copies of the builder's detailed interim accounts or by architect's certificates stating that interim payments are due to the builder.

On site, the valuer should check that the work carried out conforms to the previously approved drawings and is of a satisfactory quality. Whilst he is in no way responsible to the borrower for any supervision of the job, if there are obvious building errors, such as missed damp-proof courses, bridged cavities, defective brickwork, missed lintels, lack of sub-floor ventilation, etc., he will wish to record these in his report to the society so that they may be brought to the attention of the borrower and put right.

The valuer's other task will be to assess the proportion of the contract works that has been carried out and thence to advise the society on the proportion, in terms of percentage, of the offered further advance that can be made. A particular danger to be on the lookout for is that of a builder of dubious financial stability who submits excessive interim accounts at an early stage, and, having been paid, disappears from the job, leaving the householder to get another builder to complete the work: if this happens, the householder will almost certainly end up paying considerably more than the original contract sum.

Completion of Extensions, Improvements, etc. When the extension, improvements or repairs which are the subject of a further advance are completed the valuer will be asked to make a further inspection with a view to certifying that the work has been completed satisfactorily and recommending that the balance of the further advance may be released.

Again it will be necessary to check that the work carried out corresponds to that shown on the previously approved drawings. Where the inspection reveals that there is defective workmanship or incomplete work it will usually be appropriate to advise that the further advance may be released subject to either a retention in an appropriate sum until the outstanding work is completed or defective work put right, or subject to the borrower giving an undertaking to the society that the outstanding work will be completed or defective work made good within a specified period of time.

Stage Payments During Initial Construction. These cases are discussed in Chapter **9.4**.

Inspections on Completion of New Property. See Chapter **9.6.**

Proposed alterations by the borrower. Many mortgage deeds will include the requirement that the borrower must not carry out any alterations to the property without the approval of the building society. If a borrower applies for such approval, the society will normally instruct its valuer to investigate the proposals and advise.

Miscellaneous Re-Inspections. If, during the term of the mortgage, the property is affected by serious defects, such as settlement, or if there is serious storm or fire damage, or notice is received by the borrower that the property is to be compulsorily acquired, etc., it is likely that the building society will instruct the valuer who originally valued the property on their behalf to investigate and advise the society.

10.3. Properties in Possession

Where a borrower falls behind with his mortgage repayments it is normal for building societies to give several warnings and to exercise a degree of latitude in cases of particular hardship. However, the society must protect its depositors, and if arrears continue it will take possession of the mortgaged property in order to sell it. In these cases the property will normally be put into the hands of a local estate agent.

Section 36(1)(a) of the Building Societies Act 1962 requires the building society to take reasonable care to ensure that the price at which a property in possession is sold is the best price that can reasonably be obtained. This responsibility is discussed by Mr. Justice Vaisey in a lengthy judgment in the case of *Reliance Permanent Building Society* v. *Harwood-Stamper* (1944) Ch. 362 which contains the following statement:

"I think that the building society must now take just as much care as a trustee has always had to take in relation to trust money, so that just as when a trustee is challenged by the beneficiary to account for what he has done, so I think a building society must be prepared, when challenged by the mortgagor, to show exact particulars of the care which it has taken to make sure that the price which has been obtained for the property is the price upon which no advance was available at the moment".

As a safeguard to confirm that the price at which a property in possession is sold is in fact the best price available at the time, it is common practice for building societies to put the property in the hands of a local estate agent and to instruct their valuer to confirm that the price negotiated with a prospective purchaser by the estate agent is the best forced sale price which the property will command; or sometimes the society will ask two valuers to prepare forced sale valuations.

Unfortunately, many possession cases show evidence of gross neglect of routine maintenance and misuse of the property. Often these cases are associated with matrimonial problems, and occasionally it will be found that the borrower is in prison for some criminal activity.

The majority of properties in possession tend to be in poorer urban areas, where vandalism of empty property is rife. If maintenance has been badly neglected, decorations are filthy, gardens overgrown, fixtures and fittings damaged or removed, and the property vandalised, there is a real danger that the society may not recover the monies owing to it, although in fact most societies insure against losses on forced sales of houses in possession.

Because of vandalism and deterioration, and the fact that outstanding monies are increasing all the time by the addition of interest, it is usually necessary to sell houses in possession as quickly as possible, bearing in mind that they may have been empty for some months before the society obtained possession. In order to achieve a quick sale the price may have to be dropped to a forced-sale value, which is often up to 10% less than the open market figure, and may be as much as 20% less.

Chapter 11

The Recommendation

The survey has been done, the particulars recorded; enquiries have been made, records consulted.

The factual parts of the report form have been filled in and the valuer is now faced with making his recommendations to the society as to the suitability of the property as security for a mortgage advance. At this stage, as at every stage, the valuer must be fully aware of his duty to ensure that the savings of many depositors are going to be adequately protected in so far that the society must be able to recoup any advance that it makes, together with the expenses of a forced sale, in the event of the borrower defaulting.

It is in making the concluding recommendation of his report that the valuer has to exercise his professional skill, experience and judgment. This is the crux of the whole report. It is this that a building society manager will probably turn to first. All the society really needs to know is in this concluding paragraph. If this is wrong, it is of no avail that the house was described in minute and accurate detail.

In making his concluding observations the valuer has a number of options open to him.

". . . . suitable security for maximum advance based on the agreed purchase price". This is what everyone wants to read—vendor, purchaser, agent, building society. It enables everything to go ahead smoothly with the minimum of paperwork. Hopefully, in many areas it will be applicable in the majority of cases. The valuer should not be afraid of this recommendation and should avoid the approach that raises problems as a matter of course in every case, or causes him to be forever knocking off the odd £200, feeling that he has not done his job if he fails to note some adverse comment. It really is superfluous in a case where a small advance is required on an expensive house to be asking for an undertaking that, say, a cracked pane in the lounge be repaired within three months of purchase: and the building society manager will not thank the valuer for involving him in unnecessary paper work.

Some societies require the actual percentage of the valuation that may be advanced to be specified, together with the actual term of years, but in most cases where the property is suitable for a maximum term, the actual details can safely be left to the societies, who have their own criteria for maxima, based on the status of the applicant, the age of the property and the amount of mortgage funds available: a 90% advance over a 25 year term is common.

". . . . suitable security for maximum advance on our valuation of £x which is rather less than the proposed purchase price". This recommendation is appropriate in cases where the valuer is of the opinion that the agreed purchase price is out of line with prices achieved in similar recent sales. There are occasional cases where a particular purchaser has special reasons for paying above the market value to secure a particular property. Sometimes the valuation must be reduced because the purchase price includes carpets and other furnishings which cannot be included in the mortgage security, or a garden or garage held only on an annual tenancy.

Valuation is an inexact science. Send half a dozen valuers to the same property and you will get half a dozen different figures with the highest probably about 20% above the lowest on a standard property, and with a much greater discrepancy on an unusual one for which there are few comparables. The valuer is aware of this and in cases where only a small advance is required he will not upset an agreed purchase price merely because it is marginally above his own assessment. On the other hand, in cases where a maximum advance is required, the valuer must adopt a more cautious and conservative approach, perhaps devaluing a property which he feels is priced at the upper limit of the market.

". . . . suitable security for a mortgage advance not exceeding 50%/60%/70%/80% of valuation over a period of 10/15 years". The valuer has the option of limiting the percentage advance. This is an appropriate device in cases where a lot of the value is in finishings and fittings which could quickly deteriorate if neglected; or in cases of property situated in an area which the valuer feels may deteriorate as a result of social changes or planning proposals; or in cases of an unusual property where the valuer is unsure whether the purchase price truly reflects the market.

In a similar way the term of years may be limited, usually to either ten or fifteen. There is little point in a building society mortgage for a term less than 10 years. A restricted term may be appropriate where the valuer has reason to believe that an area may be adversely affected by planning proposals or may deteriorate after the expiry of the recommended term. There is normally little objective evidence on which to base such a recommendation and the valuer will largely rely on his experience and subjective reaction.

". . . . suitable for (maximum) advance subject to . . . ." Typical conditions might include:

". . . . subject to a satisfactory report from a chartered structural engineer in respect of the deflection of upper floors/ differential settlement/structural movement/etc.";

". . . . subject to a satisfactory report from a chartered civil engineer in respect of the design of the foundations in relation to the steeply sloping site";

". . . . subject to a satisfactory structural survey report on the property by an architect or chartered building surveyor";

". . . . subject to a satisfactory report from a mining engineer or mineral valuer";

". . . . subject to a satisfactory report by a suitable specialist firm or chartered building surveyor on the condition of the under-floor space/roof space";

". . . . subject to formal confirmation that statutory approvals have been obtained for . . . .";

". . . . subject to formal confirmation from the water authority that mains water is available or a satisfactory report from a suitably qualified person that the private water supply is of suitable purity and dependability";

". . . . subject to written confirmation from the planning authority that they will not enforce the planning condition that the property may only be occupied by someone wholly or mainly engaged in agriculture";

". . . . subject to a satisfactory drain test".

The list of possible conditions is endless. They all involve other people and expense and therefore should be used only when they are essential to protect the interests of the society: they should not be used to demonstrate the valuer's erudition or make up for his lack of confidence.

". . . . suitable security for maximum advance subject to satisfactory completion". This is the normal recommendation in respect of new houses. Interim advances to meet builders' stage payments may be required in these cases.

". . . . suitable security for (maximum) advance on our valuation of £x on completion of the work that is listed in the attached estimate/specification/schedule/drawings". This is the appropriate recommendation of major reconstruction or modernisation. These are perhaps the most complicated cases with which a surveyor has to deal. They usually require a valuation in their present unimproved condition together with a recommendation as to how much may be advanced on an interim basis, plus a valuation and recommendation on completion. Cases where there are improvement grants are referred to in Chapters 4.2 and 5—in these cases the amount of the grant is deducted from the vacant possession valuation on completion, before computing the percentage mortgage advance.

".... suitable security for (maximum) advance subject to a retention of £x until the following work is completed". Retentions are appropriate only in cases where repairs must be carried out in order to safeguard the security of the society. This category of repair often includes dry rot, woodworm, structural repairs, rising damp, significant penetrating damp, rotten gutters, suspect electric wiring, replacement of missing slates, flashings, downpipes, etc., blocked drains, pointing, external painting, provision of internal w.c. etc., and sometimes repairs to rotten window-frames and door-frames. The retention should amount to the surveyor's estimate of the cost of doing the necessary work. Where it is difficult to estimate, the valuer can call for a retention in the sum of an estimate to be obtained for the work by the applicant. In cases where extensive or costly work is obviously needed and the purchase price reflects the condition of the property, the valuer will do best to advise to the society, listing the extent of work required and requesting that the applicant be asked to obtain estimates for the work. Then the matter can be dealt with as a house to be improved, with a valuation and recommendation given subject to completion of the repairs and improvements. This is of some importance, as the agreed purchase price probably reflects the poor condition of the property and a large retention from it may well kill the sale, unnecessarily.

".... suitable security for (maximum) advance subject to the applicant(s) undertaking to do the following work within three months/six months/twelve months of completion of purchase". Undertakings are appropriate for repairs which are of a minor nature or defects not likely to worsen to the extent that they will affect the value of the security if they are not carried out. Repairs to timber work, replacement of the odd missing slate, external painting, pointing, replacement of cracked sanitary fittings, etc., are often dealt with by means of undertakings. It is not normal to make retentions or require undertakings in respect to internal decorative finishes.

The valuer is not limited to any one of the above recommendations. He can permute them in almost any combination but the aim should be to keep the recommendation as straightforward as possible. There is no merit in unnecessarily complicating the issues.

There will be cases where a property is not suitable for mortgage advance. In these cases many societies prefer a short letter saying so and briefly setting out the reasons, rather than a full report and plan.

There are many reasons why a property may be unsuitable for mortgage. The most usual are major structural defects, in particular, continuing subsidence or differential settlement, extensive dampness, unsatisfactory accommodation, poor location, uncertain future, or lack of mains services or proper sanitation. Often there will be no single reason for turning a house down but a combination of factors which taken together add up to sufficient grounds for refusing a mortgage advance. Obviously some cases will be borderline, and in these it may be prudent for the valuer to have a word with the local building society manager to see if there are any other factors which may sway his opinion one way or the other, such as finding that the applicants are longstanding and reliable members of the society who are fully aware of the problems affecting the property. Before sending off an adverse report the valuer would also be well advised to check his records, for it is not unknown for a valuer to turn down a borderline property which two years ago he advised the same society was just on the other side of the border!

Chapter 12

Professional Matters

12.1. Office Records

Good office records are essential to the work of the building society valuer. Their purpose is:

(1) To enable a quick check to be made to see if the valuer or anyone else in his office has previously been involved with the property in question. This is necessary to maintain consistency within the office and avoid the loss of confidence which can arise when a valuer reports that a property is unsuitable as security for a mortgage advance when some months earlier a colleague in the office advised that the same property was suitable for a maximum advance!

(2) To enable the valuer to compare the prices achieved in sales of similar properties in the same road, or near-by.

(3) To enable the papers relating to any previous involvement that the office has had with the property to be easily and quickly located. This is essential where a re-valuation or re-inspection has to be done. It is also very useful and will save the valuer quite a lot of time when the office receives instructions to survey a property of which it already has details.

Larger practices with multiple offices will put records onto a computer, but for the majority of offices a card-index system is the most appropriate way of indexing properties with which the office has been involved. A simple and effective system is to file by streets in alphabetical order, possibly with different cabinets for different towns. Where a street map of a borough exists, this can be used to produce a card for each road or street in the borough. Each card then needs several columns with headings as follows:

Road			District			Town			
1 Date	2 No.	3 Tenure	4 Type	5 Beds	6 C.H.	7 Garage	8 Price	9 Notes	10 Ref.

Every property with which the valuer's office is concerned can be entered onto these cards with the relevant particulars.

Column 2 will have the number of the house or the name if it has no number. Detached houses or farms in the country can be filed either under their own name or under the road which is nearest to them or on a village by village basis.

Column 3 will indicate whether the property is freehold or leasehold.

Column 4 will indicate the type of property, e.g. detached house, semi-detached house, end terraced house, mid-terraced house, detached bungalow, semi-detached bungalow, ground-floor flat, first-floor flat, etc., lock-up shop, shop with living accommodation, etc.

Column 5 shows the number of bedrooms.

Column 6 indicates whether the property has central heating or not.

Column 7 shows whether there is car space, single garage, double garage or space for a garage.

Column 8 lists the price and column 9 any relevant notes, such as "unsuitable for mortgage".

Column 10 will give the office reference to where the papers can be found. A prefix can indicate the type of involvement the office had, e.g. sale, structural survey, building society survey, valuation, etc., and in the case of a building society survey, for which society.

Because domestic property valuations are practically all carried out by the comparative method, records for the purposes of comparison are essential. In addition to records of properties handled within the office it is useful to have information on house prices from other sources. The main alternative source will be the property pages of local newspapers circulating in the area. These pages should be systematically filed in the office for reference, bearing in mind that the prices given are asking prices and not necessarily the prices achieved. Opinions will differ about the system of recording information obtained from these sources on the grounds that asking prices can be misleading. Nevertheless, such prices do give some useful background information, especially where responsible agents are involved.

Copies of building society reports prepared by the office can be filed in ring-binders or in filing cabinets. Systems of numbering and filing arrangements will differ from office to office, largely depending upon the number of societies for which the office acts and the number of surveys being handled, which can vary from the odd one a month to perhaps 20 or more a day. Where more than a nominal number of surveys are being undertaken, it is probably best to file reports for each society separately in date order, giving each a reference number with a prefix letter to denote the society. Where papers are put into files, these can be colour-coded for different societies. Whatever the details of the system adopted, the imperative requirement is that any report can be located and produced within less than a minute, so that the report is immediately available when needed, as for example when someone from the building society telephones with a query about the property.

12.2. Fees

The following fee scale has been agreed between the Building Societies Association and the professional bodies representing valuers.

Valuation of Property	Fee
Not exceeding £2,000	£5
Exceeding £2,000 but not exceeding £15,000	£5 plus £1 per £500 or part thereof in excess of £2,000
Exceeding £15,000 but not exceeding £30,000	£31 plus £1 per £1,000 or part thereof in excess of £15,000
Exceeding £30,000 but not exceeding £40,000	£46 plus £1 per £2,000 or part thereof in excess of £30,000
Exceeding £40,000	The fee to be settled by negotiation between the society and the valuer.

Re-inspection fees are also calculated on the valuation of the property, at the rate of £3 plus 5p per £100 or part thereof in excess of £5,000.

Mileage is chargeable at 10p* per mile in respect of journeys to properties situated more than 5 miles from the valuer's office. If the valuer makes more than one valuation outside the 5 miles radius on the same journey, he is to apportion the travelling allowances equitably between each case outside the radius.

All building society valuation fees, other than for surveys carried out by staff surveyors, are subject to an addition for V.A.T. at the current rate.

It will be appreciated that the re-inspection fees are very low, especially if a long journey is involved. Most of the larger societies have in fact increased the fees they pay for re-

* 17p from 1st November 1979.

inspections to at least £5.

Re-inspections are normally made to check that work has been completed satisfactorily. In other cases revaluations are called for, such as when a borrower wishes to extend his property. The work involved in revaluations can be considerable, involving an up-to-date valuation of the property in its present condition and a valuation assuming completion of the proposed works, together with an updated insurance valuation. Whilst it is true that the valuer will have some information about the property on his file, this may be many years out of date and he will often have to start again from scratch. Revaluations may strictly be charged for in accordance with the fee scale for a first valuation but the normal practice appears to be to charge rather less than this on the basis of *ad hoc* local arrangements, often the re-inspection scale but with a minimum fee of £10 or £15.

Because many societies collect survey fees in advance, it assists their book-keeping if valuers charge the precise amount the society has collected rather than making a marginal reduction in respect of any small de-valuation of the purchase price. For the same reason such offices prefer their valuers not to charge for mileage—so it becomes a matter of swings and roundabouts. This arrangement is not applicable to rural areas where distances are considerable and it would be unreasonable to expect surveyors not to charge mileage. In contrast, other societies expect the fee charged to be exactly as the scale.

If a property is clearly unsuitable for mortgage advance, most societies appreciate it if the valuer cuts short his inspection and reports by way of a brief letter only, charging a reduced fee, of say 50% of the scale.

Some societies require a valuer's invoices to be submitted quarterly, others monthly and others require an invoice to be sent with each survey report.

12.3. The Valuer's Own Insurance

There is no end to the risks that one can insure against. The following are the minimum risks against which a building society surveyor should insure.

Employer's Liability. This is a statutory requirement.

Third-party Liability. This covers damage to persons or property caused in the course of business.

Fire Insurance of Office Premises and Contents. Besides

office equipment the valuer will have many records which will take a considerable time to replace if they are destroyed. Insurance against loss of profits in case of fire should also be considered.

Burglary. Including theft of cash.

Motor Insurance. This must cover for business use. Where members of a firm are responsible for arranging their own insurance, it is prudent for the firm to carry an over-riding contingency motor policy to protect the firm in the event of a claim against a partner or member of staff who is found to have overlooked the renewal of his insurance or whose cover is inoperative for some other reason.

Theft or Loss of Equipment. This is probably worthwhile, bearing in mind that the valuer may be carrying equipment worth in excess of £250, including moisture meter, dictating machine, camera, pocket calculator, binoculars, etc.

Personal Accident. Surveying does involve risks, especially on construction sites.

Professional Indemnity. The market for indemnity insurance is very limited. Premiums vary widely, depending upon the number of staff employed, the type of work carried out and the previous claims-record. There is inevitably an excess clause, so that the valuer has to pay the first part of each and every claim. The amount of the excess varies greatly, from as little as £100 to as much as £2,500 or more.

As a condition precedent to their right to be indemnified under a policy, the insured must give to the underwriters immediate notice in writing of any claim made upon them or any occurrence of which they are aware which may subsequently give rise to a claim being made against them, and shall not have made any admission, offer or promise to settle any claim or incur any costs or expenses in connection therewith without the written consent of the underwriters.

The underwriters reserve the right to settle claims rather than contest them, which can be infuriating in the case of a claim not much above the amount of a large excess where there is an adequate defence.

The insured normally warrants "that the following clause be inserted in all survey reports issued by and on behalf of the firm except in the case of surveys undertaken for building societies, life assurance companies or other institutional lenders, provided the contents of such reports are not disclosed either orally or in writing to the prospective purchaser, 'we have not inspected woodwork or other parts of the structure which are covered, unexposed or inaccessible and we are therefore unable to report that such parts of the property are free from rot, beetle or other defects' ". Some policies also have a similar exclusion clause in respect of high alumina cement.

There is normally a requirement in indemnity policies that surveys and valuations are made by suitably qualified persons and a typical wording is, "This policy shall not afford any indemnity in respect of any claim made against the assured arising from survey and/or valuation reports unless such surveys and/or valuations shall have been made,

(a) by a partner or member of the assured's staff who has not less than five year's experience of such work with the assured firm or who is a Fellow or Associate of the Royal Institution of Chartered Surveyors or a Fellow or Associate of the Incorporated Society of Valuers and Auctioneers or by a person whose name has been submitted to the underwriters and who has received their prior approval in writing".

It is important to realise that the indemnity limit is the maximum amount the underwriters are liable for in respect of all claims made during the policy period. It is sometimes incorrectly thought that the limit is in respect of each claim that is made, with the result that some firms may find themselves under-insured. It is difficult to assess the amount of cover needed, and this will probably be dictated by other work rather than building society surveys. This is something on which the advice of a broker should be sought.

It is uncommon for claims to be made by building societies against their valuers but it can happen, and the prudent valuer will take care to have indemnity insurance. In order to succeed with a claim a building society will have to make a loss and there will have to be negligence on the part of the valuer. The most likely situation giving rise to a claim is where a valuer misses fairly clear evidence of structural settlement or subsidence at the time of his inspection and this continues to such an extent that the property becomes beyond economic repair and the insurers repudiate any liability on the grounds that there was evidence of the problem at the time the property was purchased and taken into mortgage.

Confidentiality of Reports

There is an understanding between building societies and their valuers that observations contained in valuation reports are confidential to the society and will not be disclosed to any other party. If this were not the case valuers would have to be much more guarded in the wording of their reports so as to avoid any possibility of claims from the purchaser alleging over-valuation or defects not mentioned, or claims from the vendor alleging under-valuation or an unnecessarily adverse report. Coupled with this, indemnity insurers would require reports to be hedged with standard exclusion clauses. This would not be in the interests of the society, who need a frank and forthright report on which to base their offer of advance. In addition, if reports were not confidential to the society, valuation fees would have to be increased.

Many report forms include a section for the valuer's "Confidential Observations". Other forms have a note to the effect that, "This report, which is private and confidential, is for the sole use of the Directors of the Society and its contents will not be disclosed to any other person".

The suggested mortgage application form in the BSI publication "Mortgage Lending Procedure—A model" includes the following among the declarations to be signed by the applicant(s):-

"(4) The Valuer's report is for the confidential information of the society and cannot be disclosed, and that no responsibility can be accepted by the society for the condition of the property."

Where a report form makes no mention of confidentiality, a surveyor may deem it prudent to include some appropriate wording in his report or confirm the position in a cover letter to the society.

12.4. Structural Surveys

It is important that applicants for mortgages appreciate that the building society survey is a valuation survey and not a structural survey. The fact that a building society takes a property into mortgage is no guarantee whatsoever that it is free from major defect, for, whilst the building society valuer will draw attention to any major defect which is apparent to him, he does not make the detailed examination which a structural survey involves and which is likely to take at least three times as long as a valuation survey and cost about three times as much. There are an appreciable number of cases where serious defects are not (and cannot be expected to be) picked up by the building society valuer and in the writer's opinion it is most unwise for any purchaser to buy a property without the safeguard of a structural survey.

Many building societies have in fact, for a number of years, been advising applicants that in addition to the building society valuation they should have a private structural survey for their own use. The printed literature handed out to applicants by some societies includes this advice. When an applicant has indicated that he does want to have a structural survey, the building society normally suggests that he goes to their surveyor so that the structural survey can be done at the same time as the building society valuation, in which case the overall fee will probably be rather less than if two different surveyors are appointed.

In August 1979 the Building Societies Association, after consultation with the Office of Fair Trading, recommended member societies to consider having either the valuer, while carrying out his valuation for the society, make a structural survey for the applicant for a mortgage or having the society's valuation done by a surveyor named by the applicant provided he is acceptable to the society. Societies and applicants will continue to receive separate reports and it will be necessary for those wishing to use this combined inspection to discuss the question with their societies before the latter make their own arrangements for the valuation.

It is not always appreciated that a conflict of interests can occur when a valuer is acting for both building society and applicant. The applicant is looking for the maximum mortgage he can obtain with the minimum retention, whereas the primary concern of the building society is to ensure that its depositors interests are safeguarded, often calling for a more cautious approach. For this reason societies may be prudent to limit the reports they will accept to those prepared by valuers on their own panels or at least to established local practices of good standing.

Purchasers' solicitors have a duty to advise their clients of the need for a structural survey.

The building society valuer is therefore likely to get several requests for structural surveys of properties which he is going to survey for a building society. In these cases it is up to the surveyor to agree an appropriate fee directly with the applicant.

Where a surveyor is requested to do a structural survey as a result of advice given by the building society for which he is valuing the property, it is not good enough for him merely to provide a valuation based on a survey in no greater depth than that required for a building society valuation. In this respect purchasers and building society staff should be aware that the "Inspectahome" scheme launched in July 1979 and offering a walk-round inspection by a chartered surveyor is not, and does not claim to be, a structural survey: in particular it does not include inspection of roof and sub-floor voids (which are two of the main areas where major structural defects are often found) and thus is little different from a building society valuation survey.

Fees for structural surveys vary considerably depending on the size, type and value of the property, extent and depth to which the survey is to be taken and the attitude of the practice concerned to structural surveys—many practices do not want them because of the degree of experience needed to do them, the sheer physical effort of this type of work, the lack of profitability compared with other types of work and the liability involved. Fees also vary from one part of the country to another. Text books have traditionally advised that the surveyor should make a preliminary visit to assess the work involved before quoting a fee, but this is only practical in cases of very large and expensive properties. In most cases purchasers will telephone or call at the surveyor's office to ask what a structural survey will cost and how soon it can be done. Thus some system is required to enable the surveyor's receptionist to quote a fee on the spot, with reference back to the surveyor himself only in special cases. The easiest system is to have fees based on purchase price although this is very hit and miss with, for example, a large Victorian terraced house in a run down area having a purchase price much less than a modern detached house but probably taking longer to survey. A refinement is to have fees based on purchase price but adjusted according to the age of the property, using age bands of pre–1919, 1919–1945 and post 1945.

Where a building society valuation is being carried out on the same visit as a structural survey, an addition in the region of 10–15% of the structural survey fee is appropriate to cover the additional information and report required by the building society. A printed scale of fees for structural surveys should be qualified in respect of properties over say 20 miles from the surveyor's office and properties being sold at exceptionally low figures because of special circumstances (e.g. purchase by sitting tenant). The right should be reserved not to accept instructions in any particular case: this is important as the surveyor may receive instructions to survey a property where he is already acting for the vendor.

A real problem arises as to exactly what a structural survey involves. On the one hand it is clear from the advice given by societies to their applicants that they envisage a structural survey to involve a more detailed examination of the property than is involved in a building society valuation. On the other hand a "full structural survey" is out of the question as it cannot be done without having tradesmen in attendance to expose hidden timbers, open up voids and do detailed tests of services, which is unlikely to be acceptable to the vendor, and in any case is likely to cost far more than the average purchaser is prepared to pay. It would be very helpful if some authoratative body were to define a level of structural surveys somewhere between the building society valuation and a "full structural survey", but until this is done each firm of surveyors will have to pitch its own level. (It is understood that the R.I.C.S. are working on this and hope to publish a first draft towards the end of 1979.) It is essential, for the surveyor's protection, that he should define to his client in writing before the survey is carried out the extent to which it will be taken and the limitations to which it will be subject. Limitations which are not made known before instructions are accepted may have no validity when viewed in the light of the Unfair Contract Terms Act 1977. It is also important for the surveyor to get instructions in writing.

The practice of the writers office, on receipt of an initial enquiry for a structural survey, is to send to the prospective client a scale of charges for structural surveys and an order form to be filled in and returned; together with a standard letter in the following terms:

"I refer to your recent enquiry and note that you wish us to carry out a structural survey of the house you intend to buy. We normally provide a 'Standard Structural Survey' which is intended to give an appraisal of the condition of the premises.

It is important to appreciate that what is sometimes known as a full structural survey is often not feasible, since it involves the assistance of tradesmen to expose structural timbers, provide long ladders and make engineering tests on services, etc. This type of survey requires considerable time, is costly and generally unacceptable to the vendor.

In a 'Standard Structural Survey' the limitations imposed by finishes, furnishings and limited access to voids are accepted and the assistance of tradesmen is not sought.

Nevertheless, it is our experience that such a survey makes it possible to advise, with a reasonable degree of assurance, whether the house is affected by structural defects which might be costly to repair, or might make re-sale at a later date very difficult. We have found that this type of standard structural survey meets the requirements of the vast majority of purchasers. Our charges and conditions for standard structural surveys are enclosed herewith. If you wish us to carry out the work please will you complete the attached form, giving details of the property, and return it to us. The survey will then be put in hand within the next few days".

The order form draws attention to the limitations which will be incorporated into the report—they are in fact printed on the back cover of the report. These read:

"(1) The woodwork or other parts of the building which are covered, unexposed or inaccessible to the surveyor without the assistance of a carpenter or other person have not been inspected. Where property is furnished at the time of survey those parts of the building covered by furniture and/ or floor coverings have not been fully inspected. It is not therefore possible to report conclusively that these parts of the property are free from defect.

(2) Trial holes to determine sub-soil conditions or foundation sizes, and theoretical calculations to check sizes of structural elements, have not been made. Tests to determine whether High Alumina Cement was used during construction have not been made and it is therefore not possible to state that the building is free from risk in this respect.

(3) Tests of services installations or drains involving the attendance of specialist consultants or tradesmen and/or the use of special equipment have not been carried out.

(4) Full investigation of title, tenure, covenants, rights of way, planning approvals, clearance orders, improvement lines, N.H.B.C. certificates, etc., normally involving the services of a solicitor, have not been carried out".

A survey of this type, which involves inspection of sub-floor and roof spaces where there is access to these, and opening up of manholes, is as much as most purchasers either need or are willing to pay for. Where fuller inspections are required or particular details of the property are to be inspected in greater depth, separate arrangements can of course be made.

The work involved in structural surveys is quite beyond the

scope of this book, and the reader is referred to the works listed in the next section.

12.5. The Building Society Valuer's Library

If the building society valuer is going to be able to do his job properly and to advise his clients in a manner which inspires confidence, he will need to have available a library of information to which he can turn for assistance, especially in non-standard cases.

The following are the writer's suggestions for a basic library, bearing in mind that on several subjects all that is needed is a fairly brief introduction, rather than a detailed work.

Background	Pawley —Home Ownership (The Architectural Press)
Building Societies	Building Societies Yearbook (annually—Franey & Co.) Building Societies Gazette (monthly—Franey & Co.)
Building Society Law	Wurtzburg & Mills—Building Society Law (Stevens & Sons) *Note.* Contains the text of the Building Societies Act 1962
Building Society Procedure	BSI Research Group—Mortgage Lending Procedure: A Model (The Building Societies Institute)
Law of Property	Cheshire's Modern Law of Real Property (Butterworths)
Styles in Housing	Prizeman—Your House—The Outside View (Hutchinson) Munro—English Houses (Estates Gazette)
Building Construction	Mitchell's Building Construction (5 volumes—Batsford) Everett—Materials King & Everett—Components and Finishes

Foster—Structure and
Fabric—Part 1
Foster & Harrington—Structure
and Fabric—Part 2

or

McKay—Building Construction (4
volumes—Longmans)
Registered House-Builder's
Foundation Manual—Preventing
Foundation Failures in New
Dwellings (N.H.B.C.)

Traditional Building
Construction

Mitchell—Building Construction
and Advanced Building
Construction; any of the pre-1914
editions (Batsford—only available
second-hand)

Building Services

Burberry—Environment and
Services (Mitchell's Building
Construction—Batsford)

Drainage

Woolley—Drainage Details in S.I.
Metric (Northwood Publications)
The Public Health Act 1936
(H.M.S.O.)

Easements for
Services

Wilkinson—Pipes, Mains Cables
and Sewers (Oyez)

Roads

The Highways Act 1959 (H.M.S.O.)

Building Defects and
Structural Surveying

Eldridge—Common Defects in
Buildings (Property Services
Agency—H.M.S.O.)
Melville, Gordon &
Boswood—Structural Surveys of
Dwelling Houses (Estates Gazette)
Desch—Structural Surveying
(Griffin)
Bowyer—Guide to Domestic Building

Surveys (Crosby Lockwood)
Gatwick—Dampness (Crosby
Lockwood)
Note. Eldridge and Melville, Gordon
& Boswood compliment each other;
Desch is useful on timber defects
and Bowyer provides a useful simple
introduction
Timber Defects.
Scott—Deterioration and
Preservation of Timber in Buildings
(Longmans)

Building Repairs   Melville & Gordon—The Repair and
Maintenance of Houses
(Estates Gazette)

Housing Law and   Macey & Baker—Housing
Management   Management (Estates Gazette)

Town Planning   Heap—An Outline of Planning Law
(Sweet & Maxwell)
Town and Country Planning Act
1971 (H.M.S.O.)
The General Development Order
1973 (H.M.S.O.)

Building Regulations   Whyte & Powell-Smith—The
Building Regulations Explained and
Illustrated (Granada)
The Building Regulations 1976
(H.M.S.O.)
(or the Building Standards
(Scotland) Regulations 1963)

Valuation   Lawrance, Rees & Britton—Modern
Methods of Valuation of Land,
Houses and Buildings (Estates
Gazette)
Parry's Valuation and Conversion
Tables (Estates Gazette)
Guidance Note No. A3—The
Valuation of Property Assets for
Investment and as Security for Loans
(R.I.C.S.)
The Valuation of Residential

Property—Conditions of
Engagement (R.I.C.S.)
The Estates Gazette (weekly)
The Valuer (Journal of the I.S.V.A.)
Country Life (weekly)
Local Newspapers (daily/weekly)
Local Estate Agents' lists
(weekly/monthly)
Office Records

Building Costs

Guide to House Rebuilding Costs for
Insurance Valuation
(annually—Building Cost
Information Service of the Royal
Institution of Chartered Surveyors)
Quarterly Index of Rebuilding Costs
(quarterly—B.C.I.S.: R.I.C.S.)
Crystal Smith—Estimating for
Repairs and Small New Works
(Northwood Publications)
Estimating—monthly supplement to
Building Trades Journal (Northwood
Publications)
Spon's Architects' and Builders'
Price Book (annually—E. & F. Spon)
Griffith's Building Price Book
(annually—Barton Publishers)
Laxton's Building Price Book
(annually—Kelly's Directories Ltd.)

Boundaries and
Deed Plans

Powell-Smith—Boundaries and
Fences (Butterworths)

Building
Specification

Registered House-Builder's
Handbook—Part II, Technical
Requirements for the Design and
Construction of Dwellings
(N.H.B.C.)
Bowyer—Small Works Supervision
(Architectural Press)

N.H.B.C.

Marten & Luff—Guarantees for New
Homes—A Guide to the National
House-Building Council Scheme
(Oyez)

Flats	Melville, Gordon & Boswood, op. cit. George & George—The Sale of Flats (Sweet & Maxwell)
Fire Precautions in Flats	British Standards Code of Practice CP3 Chapter IV Part 1 1971 Precautions against Fire—Flats and Maisonettes (In Blocks over Two Storeys) (B.S.I.) The Fire Precautions Act 1971 (H.M.S.O.)
Dictionaries	Scott—Dictionary of Building (Penguin)
Written English	Gowers—The Complete Plain Words (Pelican)
Maps	Street maps of local towns 1/50,000 O.S. maps of regions 1/2500 and /1250 O.S. maps as required
Local Information	Local Guide Books Local Newspapers
A Lighter View	Thelwell—This Desirable Plot (Eyre Methuen)

Index